# OUR EMERGING UNIVERSE

# OUR
# EMERGING
# UNIVERSE

## BY ALLAN BROMS

## 1961

DOUBLEDAY & COMPANY, INC., GARDEN CITY, NEW YORK

# CONTENTS

1156089

# LIST OF FIGURES

# LIST OF PLATES

# FOREWORD

OUR EMERGING UNIVERSE tells the story of physical evolution of the Universe: the galaxies and stars, our Sun and its family of attendants, and more particularly this Earth as the habitable home of life. This is the first volume of a planned series on the full story of Evolution. Because the primary purpose of the series is to give understanding, emphasis throughout is on the *reasons why* rather than the mere detailed chronicle of evolutionary events and lines of descent. When facts or the reasons why are not known, or in doubt or dispute, that is always freely admitted. For such is the way of Science, it makes no pretense whatever to knowing what is still in fact unknown. There will be some guesses, however, but they will always be labeled as such. But they too have their value, for Science does grow by wise guessing, if then followed by critical checking. Guess and check, step by step, exploringly expand, that is the way to its thrilling progress. This too is part of our story.

That story as a whole is here based in part on an old series of nearly two hundred popular radio talks I have given in the New York area, many of them coupled with trips for the public to natural history and other museums. Much also derives from articles by scientific men and my own writings in *Evolution Magazine* during the nine years I was its science editor. Everything, of course, has now been carefully brought up-to-date, and in that I have been generously helped by many scientist friends, both old and new. They are too many for proper individual acknowledgments, but where I either quote or refer to their work, I give grateful credit. They are, naturally, in no way responsible for the light manner I often use in telling my version of the story.

*Flushing, New York*                                          A.B.
*May, 1961*

# OUR EMERGING UNIVERSE

CHAPTER 1

IN THE BEGINNING

THIS is the Story of Creation as told by modern science in the light of our present knowledge of the pertinent facts.

Because the body of that knowledge is ever growing, and because thoughtful minds read variant meanings into even the self-same facts, we have differing versions here and there in the story. These we must then weigh, and when we can, choose between as we proceed with our study.

Of the very beginnings there are now two main rival versions, and these we will now consider in turn.

According to Version One, it all began with one Big Bang—our Universe in vast explosion. That was several billion years ago.

As yet, of course, there were no ears to hear, nor eyes to see. Had there been eyes, they would surely have been blinded by the all-pervading flash of brilliance, far exceeding even that of our H-bomb. Also, this was no flash of a fractional instant, but took years to dim—possibly to utter darkness.

If that darkness did come, it may well have prevailed for some tens of millions of years before the stars began to glow, and so reveal a new Universe. For in that deep darkness a chaos of exploding matter was congregating into vast galaxies, condensing into huge star masses, and shaping some quite minor attendant worlds. Thus began the evolution of our present Universe, culminating for us in our Sun to give us light and warmth, and the Earth as our habitable home.

At least that is one version worked out by some scientific men for the opening event in the shaping of stars, Sun, and Earth. There is currently, however, a rival version. That second version denies the Big Bang at the Beginning. It does accept big bangs, a series of them, all truly prodigious, yet relatively minor, and occurring from time to time even now. However, this version may require something hard to accept, a continuous creation going on now and eternally.

Each of these current versions, being formulated by scientists, has of course its facts to go on, and its points pro and con. In fact, at the present state of our scientific knowledge, we may not be able to decide between them, at least not until we learn more facts and these decide for us which version to accept. So for the moment we will give the story of Universe Creation according to Version One, in due course explain Version Two, state such facts as support and deny each, and let the new facts of further research decide between them.

Version One, of the Big Bang, suffers from a serious disadvantage. It occurred once and for all in a single unrepeated instant of the past, before which all is mystery. We cannot know how things were before the Big Bang because the explosion wiped out every trace of previous fact. What brought matter to the primal point of explosion, we do not know. Did matter and energy exist, and did they act then as they do now? We assume so, but we have no proof. One idea, offered by the Belgian mathematician Abbé Georges Lemaître in 1927, had the Big Bang start with a single, all-inclusive primeval atom, whatever that may mean. You see, scientists do speculate, but also, as scientists, they do not even pretend to really know.

However, we do have some fair evidence that the Big Bang really did occur, and even indications of its probable date. At the outset, we may quite reasonably assume that matter was already present. At the starting instant of explosion, it seems we must also assume conditions of enormous pressures and terrifically high temperatures, so that such matter could have existed only as primal protons and electrons, with a portion of these basic units unstably coupled as neutrons. Perhaps, during the initial hour of explosion, with temperatures dropping from some billions of degrees, these primal units had largely joined into the atoms of our present chemical elements, say in much the same proportions we now find prevailing in our Universe as a whole.

From such a beginning we can then go on with an ensuing chain of cosmic events leading to the state of affairs we observe as now existing. In telling that story, we will not always be certain of particulars, nor claim to be. But we can still piece it together tentatively, in the fullest possible accord with the known facts of the Universe and with the laws of Nature's behavior as we have so far learned them.

In support of the Version of the Big Bang, why do we think that the Universe did in fact explode?

Simply because, though it began so long ago, we still see this vast explosion going on.

Now obviously that needs explaining, which means first some facts to go on, and then some reasons why. But first the facts, and for these we start on a rapid survey of our Universe.

## Our Universe Today

We must needs start from our Earth, the stage on which we, and our kindred living things, play their actor parts. Yet before we set that stage, we must leave Earth briefly, largely to orient ourselves in the great Universe outside and to get some proper sense of true proportions. For as sizes go in the Universe, this world of ours is a mere midget, a seemingly solid globe only 8000 miles in diameter, and weighing a mere 6600 billion billion tons. Even in the family of nine planets circling about the Sun, it is one of the humbler members—four are many times larger and Jupiter is nearly 320 times as massive. Yet all the planets together are insignificant compared with the Sun itself, having only a small part of 1 per cent of the Sun's huge mass. That mass is in fact well over 300,000 times that of the Earth. And because of this mass, as we will discover shortly, the Sun is able to shine intensely by its own light, which none of its attendant planets can do. We see them only by reflected sunlight, their brightness to our eyes depending on their nearness to or remoteness from the Sun as source of light, on the sizes and reflecting powers of their surfaces, and of course on their ever changing distances from the Earth as they severally circle about the Sun in differing orbits and periods. Thus our Earth travels about the Sun in a year of 365 days at a mean distance of 93 million miles, while little Mercury, at 40 per cent the distance, takes only 88 days, and Pluto, at 40 times the Earth's distance, needs 248 years for each circuit.

Today we know that our Sun is just a star, so very bright to us only because of its nearness. Despite its huge mass, it is actually below average in star mass and luminosity. For instance, Sirius, the brightest other star in our sky, is 2.4 times as massive and 26 times as luminous. Yet this is only average, falling between the extremes of giant and dwarf stars. Thus the star S Doradus, which because of distance is not even visible to the naked eye, is probably fifty times the Sun in mass and a million times as luminous. On the other hand, the near but dim star BD4°4048B, of unknown mass, is a mere 1/600,000 the Sun in luminosity. The sizes and densities of stars also vary considerably, with our Sun again near average. Thus the Red-Giant Antares of our summer evening skies is actually 230 times the Sun in diameter, which means roughly ten million times in volume, but (except perhaps toward its center) is of such low density that we would consider it virtually a vacuum. At the other extreme are such White Dwarfs as the dim companion of Sirius, not much larger than the Earth, but packed so densely that a cubic inch contains about a ton of matter, this being possible only because its atoms have been crushed by stripping away their encircling electrons. But these extremes are both rare, and nearly all the visible stars are normal suns much like our own.

On a clear dark moonless night we can see between two and three thousand stars at one time, and there are nearly five thousand visible to the naked eye over the entire sky. But these are only the very near neighbor stars. With our giant telescopes we can today distinguish a couple of billion, especially by long exposures on sensitive photographic plates, and so map our sky in remarkable detail. For example, the naked eye sees a broad irregular band of misty light stretching across the firmament. This band is the Milky Way. Our telescope-cameras reveal it to be made up of myriads of faint stars, here and there obscured by great clouds of dust and gas called nebulae, some dark, others more or less illuminated by nearby stars. It was early surmised that our universe of stars was shaped like a great disc and that we, viewing it from the inside, saw more stars toward its center and out toward its edges than in other directions. After more than a century of difficult but progressively successful measuring and estimating of star distances, we have confirmed this grouping of the stars about us, and can guess at their numbers and the dimensions of this Milky Way disc. In it are probably a hundred billion stars, and the disc itself is perhaps 100,000 light years across and about one-tenth as thick, with our Sun well out toward one edge. (A light year is the distance traveled by light in one year, at the speed of 186,000 miles per second, and is equal to nearly six million million miles.) The very nearest star turns out to be a dim one in our southern sky, Proxima Centauri, four and a third light years away, which gives an idea how thinly the stars are scattered through space, even in our seemingly crowded sky. As for the Milky Way disc, its width in miles comes out as six followed be seventeen zeros, a number much too awkward to handle and of course altogether too huge for the mind to grasp.

### Outside Our Milky Way

Yet now, despite its vast dimensions, we call the Milky Way, not our Universe, but merely our Galaxy. For as we peer out between its seemingly concentrated, yet scattered stars, we see at even greater distances other vast gatherings of stars and dust clouds of comparable dimensions. Some few are quite shapeless, others round or oblong. Most, however, are flattened discs, roughly lens-shaped, as we see from those we can view edgewise. Viewed at an angle or full-face, they usually reveal more or less a two-armed spiral structure, and have therefore come to be known as spiral galaxies. Both shape and structure suggest a slow rotation of each spiraled lens on its axis, and this has been confirmed in various ways, both for these distant galaxies and our own. Of course the rates of rotation vary, being apparently 19,000,000 years for the great Andromeda spiral, (Plate I) and some 200,000,000 years for our own Milky Way system. Also the rotation is faster nearer the center and slower farther out, which is exactly what physical theory leads us to expect.

So the horizons of our visible Universe are being greatly expanded, being limited largely by the light-grasp of our great telescope-cameras. At present we can reach out visually to a distance of two billion light years, and photograph a couple of billion galaxies averaging somewhat smaller than our own. And we may be quite sure that with instruments of even greater light-grasp, or with our present telescopes aided by the new electronic intensifiers, our reach will be further extended and the number of visible galaxies multiplied many times. Even now our new giant radio telescopes are extending the horizons of our total Universe and giving us information of new kinds both to illuminate and to puzzle our understanding.

At first, when we knew comparatively few galaxies, they seemed to be scattered quite at random. But as our more powerful instruments multipled them to the thousands, and our knowledge of their distances grew, it became evident that they are grouped in a dozen or so clusters. Thus our own Milky Way belongs to a small Local Group including the two Magellanic Clouds of our southern sky (about 150,000 and 170,000 light years away, (Plate II) the giant spiral M 31 in Andromeda (1,600,000 or more light years distant), accompanied by a small oblong galaxy M 32 nearby, the great open Triangulum spiral M 33, (Plate IV) the spindle-shaped Virgo spiral NGC 4594 seen edgewise, (Plate III) and another

dozen or so in our vicinity, all within a space-sphere a couple
of million light years in diameter.

This Local Group should perhaps be considered part of the
great Virgo cluster of more than a thousand members, cen-
tered some 22 million light years away. This is rivaled in
numbers by only the Coma cluster some 137 million light
years distant. The whole list of galactic clusters is tabulated
below, as to distances, membership when known, and other
data shortly to prove revealing.

TABLE OF THE GALACTIC CLUSTERS

| Cluster | Member-ship | Distances in Million Light Years | Recession in Mi. per Sec | Ratio of Recession /Distance | Age in Billions of Years |
|---|---|---|---|---|---|
| Local Group | 19 | | | | |
| Virgo | 1000+ | 22 | 750 | 34.1 | 5.4 |
| Pegasus | | 68 | 2400 | 35.3 | 5.3 |
| Perseus | 500 | 108 | 3200 | 29.6 | 6.3 |
| Coma Berenices | 1000+ | 137 | 4700 | 34.3 | 5.4 |
| Ursa Major №1 | 300 | 255 | 9300 | 36.4 | 5.1 |
| Leo | 300 | 315 | 12000 | 38.1 | 4.9 |
| Corona Borealis | 400 | 390 | 13400 | 34.4 | 5.4 |
| Gemini | | 405 | 14400 | 35.5 | 5.2 |
| Bootes | | 685 | 24400 | 35.8 | 5.2 |
| Ursa Major №2 | | 700 | 26000 | 37.2 | 5.0 |
| Hydra | | 1100 | 38000 | 34.6 | 5.4 |
| | | | Averages | 35.02 | 5.3 |

Lately a suspicion has arisen that the galactic clusters may
themselves be arranged in a supergalactic disc, its core represented by the Local, Virgo, and Ursa Major №1 clusters. Thus
John Kraus and Hsien-Ching Ko, radio astronomers at Ohio
State University, recently found the dim glow of a radio belt
(confirmed and extended by British workers) which indicates
such a supergalaxy. This idea has now been given more definite

form by Gerard da Vaucouleurs, the Yale astronomer working at Canberra Observatory in Australia, who visions a super-galactic disc forty million light years across, with the Virgo cluster at its core and our Milky Way near its rim, spinning about at some two and one-half million miles per hour. This, however, must still be considered an unproved theory, being flatly rejected by many authorities.

Everyone understands that our giant telescopes are just huge eyes which gather much more light and so permit great magnification for viewing (and photographing) dim and mi-nute-looking objects in the sky. But less understood is that other important instrument of astronomy, the spectroscope. It works like an ordinary glass prism which spreads out white light into the colors of the rainbow. This band of colors is called the spectrum, the visible part of which extends from the red (produced by longer light waves) through orange, yellow, green, blue, and indigo to violet (produced by shorter light waves). Still shorter waves extend the spectrum invisibly into the ultraviolet, revealed by photographic and other effects, while longer waves extend it beyond the red end as infrared heat. And well beyond that fall the long radio waves with which we of late have been probing out deeply into the Uni-verse toward new and startling revelations.

In the spectroscope, to prevent overlapping of the colors, only a minute star image or a narrow slit of light is spread out by its wave lengths. The spectrum then usually shows a series of bright crosslines or a corresponding series of dark lines. The former indicates light coming directly from its source, such as a glowing gaseous nebula. The latter indicates absorption by something intervening, such as the chromosphere layer over-lying the light-giving photosphere layer of our Sun's atmos-phere. The patterns of the lines disclose many important things to trained eyes. Primarily they reveal the chemical elements or compounds giving out or absorbing the light, and much about their physical state or atomic disturbance, usually resulting from high temperatures and pressures, electromagnetic forces, etc. Thus we can analyze the surface chemistry of the stars, and classify them into meaningful groups distinguished by line patterns, predominant colors, and related surface temperatures.

We can even determine the speeds at which the stars and other celestial objects move from or toward us. Since the light-waves from a receding object seem lengthened because each succeeding wave starts farther away and is therefore delayed in reaching us, the result is a measurable shift of its spectrum lines toward the red. Conversely the lines from an approaching object are likewise shifted, but toward the violet, the amount of shift again indicating the speed of approach.

### The Exploding Universe

Right now this determination of movement from or toward us is of basic importance in our story of cosmic evolution. For when we combine the giant telescope and the revealing spectroscope, and turn them to analyze the light from the distant spiral and other galaxies, we discover an astounding fact. With only nearby exceptions, the galaxies are rushing away from us at high speeds, and the farther away they are, the higher the speeds. (Plate V) Unless the observed red shifts are due to some unknown cause depending upon distance, this means that (as a whole) the galaxies are rushing rapidly away from each other, and that our Greater Universe is literally "expanding." Considering the speeds involved—up to tens of thousands of miles per second—"expanding" seems to be gross understatement, and the proper word should be "exploding." At any rate that is what was meant earlier when it was stated that we still see a great explosion going on, which is, of course, the "fair evidence" that the Big Bang actually did occur.

As to the probable date of the Big Bang, we get at it rather simply. We just divide the distances of the several galaxies (say in millions of miles) by their respective recessions per year (also in millions of miles) to get the number of years in the past when the galaxies were presumably packed closely together and the great explosion began. There are some corrections to be applied to get the proper date, one such being the fact that we see a galaxy a billion light years away not at its present distance and recession speed, but as it was a billion years ago. Taking our table at face value, our date then comes out somewhat over five billion years ago. This corresponds fairly well with the results of other methods of dating the beginnings of our cosmic evolution which rather consistently point to such an early date. In the Table of Galactic Clusters are shown their several estimated distances, their rates of recession, ratios of rates to distances, and finally the age thus indicated in billions of years for each cluster since the Big Bang. You will note some differences in the ratios and ages in the last two columns, but actually they are surprisingly close, considering the uncertainties of the facts on which they are based. For one thing, we have no direct way of measuring the distances of these extremely remote galaxies, and must rely on estimates in which wide margins of error should be allowed. Also the measurement of the recession rates from the spectrum shifts is most difficult, for the galaxies involved are most minute and dim even in our very biggest telescopes, and their spectra are only about an eighth of an inch in length on the photographic plate, so the shifts must actually be measured under the microscope. Under these circumstances, we should emphasize the consistency, rather than the differences, between the ages indicated, for the consistency is really remarkable, pointing to a date for the Big Bang some five to six billion years ago.

At this writing, a remarkable achievement has just been reported, that Dr. Rudolph Minkowski, using the great 200-inch Palomar telescope, has succeeded in photographing a pair of galaxies in collision and apparently six billion light years distant. This object shows a recession shift so great that the invisible ultraviolet lines appear in the green position, indicating a recession velocity of 90,000 miles per second. This and the distance indicate the lapse of more than twelve billion years since the Big Bang. This is inconsistent with the five or six billion years worked out from the Table of Galactic Clusters. However, there has been a recent important revision of all estimates of galactic distances which makes the new earlier date more probable, and it now seems proper to assume that some twelve to thirteen billion years have actually passed since the Big Bang began.

What happened in those twelve or thirteen billion years? How, out of the chaos of the Big Bang, did galaxies, stars, and planets evolve? With the rapid growth in recent years of our knowledge of the pertinent facts and the underlying physical laws involved, a fairly coherent answer has been emerging. It must be admitted that some of the facts remain unexplained, and others a bit troublesome, yet on the whole the answer seems right enough—if the Big Bang actually did occur. Many workers in science have contributed to that answer. For one good and authoritative popular account, read *The Creation of the Universe* by the physicist George Gamow, but in reading it, bear in mind that the dates involved have recently been pushed back considerably earlier than those he gives. Meanwhile here are the main developments in this cosmic story.

Just before the Big Bang, it seems possible there was a Big Squeeze. We do not really know, but it may well have been due to a Big Collapse of an older, perhaps dead, Universe. The matter comprising it, pulled toward an over-all gravitational center, would have been falling together faster and faster, finally meeting at high velocities, and therefore with enormous momentums driving everything forcibly into a central mass of such high density as to break down all the elements into their primal protons and electrons. Gamow estimates that all the matter of the Universe now visible to the great 200-inch Palomar telescope could have been thus packed into a sphere about twenty-five million miles in diameter, but of course that is just a wild guess, as he would be the first to admit.

One inevitable effect of any such dense packing of matter would have been a terrific rise in temperature and therefore in luminosity. The fast-falling masses, suddenly meeting and stopping, had their enormous momentums instantly converted into the energies of heat, light, and other radiations. Gamow estimates that at maximum density, the temperatures must have been above 15 billion degrees on the Absolute scale (27 billion degrees Fahrenheit). That means that every particle of matter was rushing about at top speed, with the only way of final escape outward. The result was a violent explosion, the Big Bang. For though the momentums of gravitational falling may have brought the packed matter densely together, gravitation was then unable to hold it together against the heat, light, and other radiant energies driving it asunder.

By such an explosion, the process of energy conversion would be reversed, with the radiant energies being converted into momentums of masses flying apart. So the temperatures dropped, at first rapidly, later more slowly. Gamow figures a drop from 15 billion to 3 million degrees Absolute in the first year, then down to 3000° in the first million years, and finally after several billion years down to the average present temperature of matter in space, about 50° Absolute (370° below zero Fahrenheit).

**Formation of the Elements**

During the very first hour of explosion something very vital is thought to have happened. According to studies by Fermi, Turkevitch, Gamow, and others, it was during this brief period of sharp drops in density and temperature that the primal protons and neutrons found just the right, but transitory, conditions for joining to form the nuclei of our various chemical elements in about the relative proportions found in our Universe as a whole. Those proportions are estimated at about 99 per cent for hydrogen and helium together, and only 1 per cent for the aggregate mass of all the heavier elements up to thorium and uranium at the very limits of atomic stability. Such nuclei would quickly capture free electrons and thus form the normal atoms of the chemical elements as we know them.

Hydrogen was certainly the most abundant, for a very simple reason. One single proton makes up the ordinary hydrogen nucleus, becoming a complete atom merely by capturing a single encircling electron. Rarely, one neutron added to the proton nucleus (with one encircling electron), makes deuterium (double-weight hydrogen). One more neutron in the nucleus (with still only one electron) results in tritium (the even rarer triple-weight hydrogen). Inevitably, ordinary hydrogen became the most abundant element.

The atom of helium (next in abundance) has a nucleus of two protons and two neutrons controlling two encircling electrons, and it therefore, had to be built up, either in this initial hour of cosmic explosion or somehow later. However such fusion is comparatively easy to bring about, since even we do it in our H-bombs. What makes it easy is that a great amount of energy is released by the fusion, and the reason for that is well understood. One atom of hydrogen has a mass expressed by the figure 1.0081. The corresponding atomic mass of helium is 4.003. But this is less than four times the hydrogen mass, which is $4 \times 1.0081 = 4.0324$. In other words, in fusing four hydrogen atoms into one helium atom, there is a definite loss of mass, which is converted into energy. This release of energy is clearly what makes the H-bomb a bomb, and made easy the building up of an abundance of helium during the Big Bang, or later. In building up the still heavier elements, however, there is comparatively less and less further release of energy by loss of mass, until, for the heaviest elements, the building up actually uses up energy. This makes the heavier elements progressively harder to produce, and relatively small amounts actually come into existence.

Furthermore, the formation of much helium releases a great flood of energy, raising temperatures temporarily, and adding force to the explosion, projecting matter outward into space at even higher velocities. Against such explosive force, gravitation would seem to have no chance, not even at its strongest when the matter of the Universe was still concentrated close to its gravitational center. And apparently, as the matter became more and more widely dispersed, the central gravitational pull would be so weakened by distance that today it could never stop the scattering galaxies in their headlong flights outward and away into the depths of space.

**The Oscillating Universe**

However, there is another side to that story. Ernst J. Öpik of Armagh Observatory, North Ireland, has shown how gravitation may, in the end, overcome the momentums of the scattering galaxies, and draw them back eventually in another Big Collapse and ultimate Big Squeeze preliminary to another Big Bang. It all depends, he points out, on the amount of matter in the Universe per unit of space, in other words on the average density of that matter, upon which depends the strength of the gravitational pull available for stopping the galaxies in their headlong flights. Hitherto, the estimates of the density of matter throughout the visible Universe have been based too largely on the amounts we can see in the shining stars, which are not enough to stop the everlasting expansion we seem to be seeing. But he calls attention to the vast amount of interstellar dark matter which we do not see, but can detect by spectroscopic and other studies, the estimates of which have run as high as twenty-five times the amount visible in the stars. Astronomer Martin Schwarzschild of Princeton University has just reported a more conservative estimate of only ten times. But using an even lower ratio, Öpik concludes that there is plenty matter in the Universe to give more than enough density to ensure a gravitational stopping of the present expansion and the starting of the Big Collapse which would begin another cycle of squeeze, explosion, and expansion, ending with stoppage, collapse, etc. His guess is that the cycle repeats about every thirty billion years, that the next Big Bang is due in about twenty-five billion years hence, and that the Universe is therefore an Oscillating one, repeating its grand cycle everlastingly.

But to return to our own latest Big Bang of the past, it would seem that all matter would be blasted into its very atoms as an all-pervading gas. But rapid expansion meant rapid cooling, until matter ceased to glow, and utter darkness set in. That darkness would then prevail until somehow the thin gas could condense into stars massive enough to heat up and glow. Gamow estimates that this night of deep darkness lasted about thirty million years, during which time the only thing happening was the congregating of galaxies and star masses.

Because such cosmic congregating (particularly its very beginnings) has turned out to be a rather formidable scientific problem, we will give it the whole next chapter. But meanwhile we must note some scientific doubts about the Big Bang, as it would not be fair and proper to leave you thinking it has been accepted as unquestionable truth.

### The Steady-State Universe

The doubts of the Big Bang theory were first expressed in 1948 by two brilliant British theorists, Herman Bondi and Thomas Gold, and then argued most vigorously by the English astronomer, Fred Hoyle. He stated these doubts rather broadly in a popular book, *The Nature of the Universe*, following it in more detail with another, *The Frontiers of Astronomy*, and a great many technical articles. He starts with the same broad description of the Universe and its apparent expansion, but then reaches conclusions which are amazingly different. Thus he does not believe at all in the Big Bang, but pictures instead what is called a Steady-State Universe, which is, so to speak, continuously reproducing itself. As part of this, he thinks that matter (specifically hydrogen) is being slowly created right now throughout the spaces of the Universe, and explains that the Universe is in fact expanding precisely because this new matter is continuously intruding. He does not tell us how this new matter comes into being, but asks us (at least for the time being) to take its gradual creation on faith (scientific faith, that is), which of course means that we will take it all back the instant any positive fact gives us the slightest excuse. Furthermore, he does not explain why this accumulating of new matter should push the older matter more and more apart to give us the expanding Universe, but again asks for another bit of scientific faith, subject to the same proviso. And when we look dubious over taking so much on faith, he properly reminds us that we ourselves have no way of explaining how matter otherwise came to be (even originally, suddenly, and in a lump), and that we are taking the Big Bang itself very nearly on faith.

Naturally, as he dismisses the Big Bang and all that went with it, Hoyle contends that there was no transitory stage of terrific temperatures suitable for the building up of the 1 per cent of the heavier elements. Instead he believes that such elements are even now being formed within stars of unusually high interior temperatures, being then ejected into space by dissipation or explosion of these stars, which may be quite possible, as we shall see.

Quite obviously here is a very basic difference of opinion as to how our story of cosmic beginnings should be told. And which theory we finally decide upon will probably determine what we may then think about many further details of the story. So the question inevitably follows: Is there any test by which we can decide with reasonable certainty between the opposing theories of the Big Bang on the one hand and the Steady-State Universe on the other?

The eminent radio astronomer of Cambridge University, Dr. Martin Ryle, thought in 1955 that he had found such a test, and that he also had the proper data for making it. He based the test on the differing distributions of matter which should result from the Big Bang and the Steady-State formation of the Universe. Simply put, the latter method of formation should produce a uniform average distribution of celestial matter throughout its entire extent. And Dr. Ryle concluded that the existing data on some two thousand "radio stars" indicated instead a sparser distribution near the center of the Universe as we observe it, and a denser distribution out toward its apparent limits. This would not be consistent with the Steady-State Universe, and so would tend to support the theory of the Big Bang.

But why should Dr. Ryle thus base his test on a mere couple of thousand radio stars, when our great optical telescope-cameras reveal millions of visible galaxies scattered through space? The answer is that the radio telescopes actually penetrate several times farther out into space, and so give a better over-all picture of the distribution of matter.

However, it soon turned out that his test data was very much in error; he had literally too many radio stars. For with the further development (first in Australia) of more precise radio telescopes, about half his radio stars proved to be non-existent, having been originally recorded by combinations of nearby radio beams resulting in what we may call false images. And even this was not the end, for at present the number of actual radio stars has been further reduced (and by Dr. Ryle himself) to about 450. But it should also be noted that the Ryle test, using these fewer, but authentic, radio stars, still favors the Big Bang as against the Steady-State Universe.

Of those radio stars, only a very few can be identified with objects visible to the telescope-cameras. Spotting them precisely in the sky by radio presents one difficulty, but the major reason for not finding them visually is that they are too far away or too dim, even though they are nevertheless powerful radio transmitters. Some also are probably hidden from view behind dust clouds which obstruct their light, but not their radio signals. Though they therefore tell us far less than we would wish, they do extend our knowledge somewhat deeper into the wide-spreading Universe. Even so, it is estimated that the most remote of those recorded are only 550 million light years away, and that this is only a twentieth of the distance we should be able to see if we had adequately powerful instruments.

But why, you may ask, should there be any limit to the eventual distance we can see with bigger and better instruments? The answer lies in that expansion of the Universe which we observe, in which the recessions of the galaxies speed up as their distance from us increases. Ultimately we must come to a distance at which the galaxies will be receding at the speed of light. At that point they will simply disappear from our view, as no light wave will then be able to follow up the one before it so as to build up a continuing image of any galaxy. That ultimate distance of visibility is about ten billion light years, beyond which we will not be able to see such an expanding universe, however far it may actually extend. Whether it does so extend we do not now know, but if it does, we can picture in imagination a universe continually spilling over into invisibility. The Steady-State Universe does seem to imply that sort of a picture. On the other hand, depending on how long ago the Big Bang occurred, we may have a Universe still so young that it has not yet expanded to such limits of visibility. If so, our future improved instruments (optical or radio) may become so powerful that we will be able to see the very front of the expansion, and thus settle for good the issue between the two theories of one great primal explosion as against a continuous and eternal creation.

CHAPTER **2**

# OUT OF THE CHAOS

SCIENCE is generally supposed to solve problems, and that is its ultimate business. But often also it creates problems. That is because, in seeking answers, Science digs up new facts, and while these may provide answers to previous questions, they often present new mysteries demanding further answers. As a result, we of today have certainly many more known problems to solve than our ancestors before us. But that really means only that we have dug deeper into things, and have advanced both in the answers we have found and the more detailed questions we have learned to ask. In short, we are penetrating below the merely obvious and superficial, and farther into the realities behind all things. So our actual insight is deeper and truer, and ever more useful as we apply our new, more profound knowledge in so-called practical ways.

For example, if we begin with the Big Bang—the Universe had been blown into small smithereens, and those smithereens projected at violent velocities outward into space as an ever expanding and all-pervading gas. That happened some billions of years ago, and is still going on. But in the meantime, somehow, the exploding matter has congregated into huge galaxies consisting of myriads of hot shining stars, here and there some vast clouds of cooler gas and dust, and about many of the stars perhaps small dark planets circling in captive attendance. Science inevitably asks, "How come?" And usually, without hesitation, we answer, "That's easy. Gravitation simply draws matter together."

But the answer is not really so easy. As the knowing scientist must say, "That all depends," mostly on the state of affairs at the start. Thus, as early as 1692, Isaac Newton, writing to an associate at Cambridge University, pointed out that it made a difference whether the original matter was spread out through finite or infinite space.

"It seems to me that if the matter of our sun and planets, and all the matter of the universe, were evenly scattered throughout all the heavens, and every particle had an innate gravity towards all the rest, and the whole space throughout which this matter was scattered was finite, the matter on the outside of this space would, by its gravity, tend towards all the matter on the inside, and by consequence fall down into the middle of the whole space, and there compose one great spherical mass. But if the matter were evenly disposed throughout an infinite space, it could never convene into one mass, but some of it would convene into one mass, and some into another, so as to make an infinite number of great masses, scattered great distances from one another throughout all that infinite space. And thus might the sun and fixed stars be formed, supposing the matter were of a lucid nature."

Modern mathematical astronomers, as Sir James H. Jeans of England and Edwin P. Hubble of the United States, have in general confirmed Newton's conclusion that matter, though spread evenly throughout space, must be gravitationally unstable, and so tend to break up into separate aggregates. They further found that the sizes of the resulting aggregates would depend on the density and temperature of the original distributed matter. At the densities and temperatures indicated by recent observations, such an aggregate could form only from a mass of matter equal to at least hundreds of millions of average stars, and therefore of about the size of an ordinary galaxy.

## Factors Favoring Expansion

But note that the original matter described by Newton was in a state of quiet and even distribution through space, tending only to gravitate toward one or more centers of aggregation. But actually we find a very different state of affairs, a Universe expanding at high velocities, in the midst of violent explosive motions. And that, obviously, introduces most serious complications.

For one thing, any particle of matter, however small, has inertia. As Newton himself discovered, it will stand still, or move at constant speed in the same direction, unless its speed or direction (or state of rest) is changed by application of an outside force. Thus exploding matter will keep moving outward and away, unless slowed up, stopped, or changed in direction, by some such force as gravitation. In our expanding Universe, the inertias of its outward rushing myriads of galaxies are so great that its expansive movements can perhaps never be stopped. Gravitational pull may have slowed up the retreating galaxies somewhat, but it has not been sufficiently strong at any time (and may not be in the foreseeable future) actually to stop and then draw them back from their eternal expansion.

Now we really know very little about gravitation. Thus we certainly do not know what causes it, though it is said that some two hundred different explanations have been offered, many most fantastic, and none really satisfying. Otherwise the little we really do know about gravitation proves to be very illuminating and useful. For one thing, we are pretty sure that it operates at even the greatest distances, for every astronomical test, from Newton to our own day, indicates that. Also we reasonably assume that it always has and always will operate without let-up. Finally we do know precisely just how it behaves. That behavior was progressively discovered and formulated in the seventeenth century by Galileo, Kepler, and Newton, and has been overwhelmingly verified since. As summed up by Newton, the force of gravitation varies as the product of the masses involved, and inversely as the square of their distances apart. Thus if our Earth and Moon had each twice the mass, the force of gravity between them would be, not twice, but $2 \times 2 = 4$ times what it now is. But distance apart also counts, distance weakening the force of gravitation. The rule is that gravitation weakens as the square of the distance. Thus if Earth and Moon were twice as far apart (measured center to center), their mutual pull on each other would be less, not greater, and would be not one-half, but $\frac{1}{2 \times 2} = \frac{1}{4}$. For the convenience of the astronomer working out problems in what is known as celestial mechanics, all this is put together in a single formula. We might write it thus:

$g = \frac{M \times m}{D \times D}$. The astronomer, however, would probably write it more concisely, thus: $g = Mm/D^2$.

Now one significant thing that we must gather from this formula is that even a lot of matter, if widely and very thinly scattered as fine dust and gas, has very little gravitational power to pull itself together, there being no great concentrated masses close enough together to build up such strong gravitational power.

Making things even worse, matter in the gaseous state con-

sists of minute particles (atoms and molecules), each with
its own inertia of motion, all darting about at high individual
speeds in every direction, constantly colliding and bouncing
off in new directions, and so always tending to expand, and if
possible, escape outward. The higher the temperature, the
higher the average speeds and the greater the tendency to expand and escape. Especially in the early stages of explosion,
right after the Big Bang, when the temperatures would be the
very highest, and the gas velocities (as well as the explosion
velocities) the greatest, the expansive forces (both gaseous
and explosive) would be most powerful. So in those early
stages at least, cosmic condensation would be most unlikely.
Unfortunately, even later, condensation would remain difficult, for as expansion proceeded, distances between particles
would increase and their mutual gravitation weaken. And
with matter in the gaseous state, even in comparatively sta-
tionary clouds, the dominating tendency would be expansion
rather than condensation.

### Factors Favoring Congregation

On the other hand, it should be noted that merely explosive
movement of matter, while preventing condensation into one
central whole, would not prevent the drawing together by
gravitation of particles which were here and there streaming
along together in nearly parallel paths and at much the same
speeds. They could gather together en route, if gaseous expansion did not prevent this process.

The cooling of matter was probably a vital early factor in
making congregating possible. For one thing, some hot gases
could then cool and condense into liquids or freeze into
solids, thus losing their expansive force. Also, as atoms cooled,

many could combine chemically into stable molecules, and these then liquefy or solidify, or stick together as drops, dust, or other particles of ever growing sizes. In other words, chemical affinity and physical adhesion could aid gravitational pull to build up ever larger units of matter.

Another factor of undoubted importance would be the fact that an explosion is never a smooth and orderly process. The Big Bang was surely completely chaotic, projecting its matter and energies unevenly at varying velocities and densities, spreading generally outward, but most irregularly. In such a chaos of shifting motions and relations, momentary accidental condensations were bound to occur. But any condensation of matter, however caused, would mean a like concentration of gravitational force tending to hold the condensation permanently together. Of course the gravitational force might not prevail, if the matter were too gaseous, hot, and expansive, or the gross movements too violent and disruptive.

Yet, now and then, here and there, gravitation would prevail to hold together concentrations of great enough mass packed densely enough to hold together, the gravitational force being thus multiplied by both increase in mass and nearness to the gravitational center. Then, in due course, more matter would be drawn in, adding to the gravitating mass and its central pull. But at the very start, physical theory does demand a certain minimum massiveness if the aggregation is to hold together by sheer gravitational pull. The actual masses of galaxies have been found to meet this initial requirement, being always somewhat greater in mass than this theoretical minimum.

As Newton indicated, one broad effect of such gravitational congregating is to gather matter into *separate* aggregations, each with its own center of gravitational pull, and each gradually growing by drawing in nearby and passing matter until the spaces between the aggregates become relatively empty. In the light of the more limited knowledge of his day, Newton assumed that the resulting primary aggregates would become "sun and fixed stars." Now we realize that initially the separated units could be no less than entire galaxies, with the stars, and even their clusters, as secondary formations within the galaxies.

### Forming the Spirals

One inevitable effect of the chaotic movements following the Big Bang must have been the formation of swirls, great and small, some violent, others moderate, in the expanding cosmic matter. Any such swirl of unconfined matter in space must, however, have been a rotation of that matter about a gravitational center which had been produced by a congregating of the mass of that matter. Furthermore, in such a swirl, the central gravitational pull must have been strong enough to retain that matter against the centrifugal force of its rotation. For the momentum (inertia) of each bit of moving matter, large or small, tends to drive it straight ahead, and therefore off and away into space. To capture and retain any particle of moving matter takes a pulling force, in this case gravitation, to turn it from its straight path of escape and into an orbit of revolution about the gravitational center of the mass as a whole, or into the very mass itself. It follows, of course, that the more violent the swirl, the greater must be the galactic mass required to prevent disruption by centrifugal force. In general, therefore, slowly rotating galaxies of indefinite, round, or oblong shape can be theoretically smaller without disruption, while rapidly rotating disc-shaped spirals must be more massive to hold together or more concentrated to intensify the central pull.

However, this does not establish any known scale of sizes for the different forms. For one thing, it does not prevent slowly rotating galaxies from congregating in the larger sizes. And also, once congregated, smaller galaxies can still hold together if they are more closely packed so as to intensify gravitational pull by nearness together. Thus we find that the galaxies come in a really wide range of sizes. The only apparent effect is that the proportion of large over small galaxies does seem to increase with distance, but this can obviously be mere seeming, because at the greater distances, we can still see the larger ones, but fewer and fewer of the smaller ones, even though they are all there in much the same proportions.

### Shapes of Galaxies

Apparently more significant are the differences in shape and internal structure. As to shape, some are most irregular, their very shapelessness suggesting lack of development in gravitational organization. Evidently better organized are the round and elliptical galaxies, each with a presumed center of gravitational attraction and some degree of rotational motion. Certainly the seemingly elliptical ones are rotating and in consequence bulging at their equators. One suspects that their shapes are actually not ellipsoidal, but probably oblate (flattened at the rotational poles), though when seen edgewise they do appear elliptical. If, on the other hand, we see them from a poleward direction, they must appear deceptively round. Of course some may in fact be truly or nearly globular, if their rotations are very slow and their equatorial bulgings slight.

Apart from mere appearance to our eyes, the true oblateness of a galaxy will naturally depend on its speed of rotation relative to size. The higher the speed, the greater the equatorial bulge and polar flattening. High or low rotational speed may, of course, depend in the first instance merely on high or low initial speed in the original swirl of the condensing gravitational aggregation. But also it may well increase with time, for if condensing means shrinking in over-all size, then there should be increase in rotation speed, and therefore in oblateness.

There is a limit, however, to growth in simple oblateness. For physical theory demands that when the equatorial bulge becomes too large, its edge becomes sharp and the galaxy lens-shaped. With still faster rotation, the equatorial edge spreads out into an increasingly flattened disc about a more or less globular core. These structures are often very apparent when seen edgewise, as in the Sombrero galaxy NGC 4594 in the constellation Virgo (Plate III), and NGC 4565 in Coma Berenices (Plate VI). In both, the dark equatorial belt consists of cooler gas and dust forming an edge of obscuring clouds about the swirling mass.

Seen flat (from a poleward direction) or tilted, the details of such a spreading disc become clearer, and normally reveal a spiral structure, with opposite arms spiraling outward from the central core. Plate I shows a photograph of the great Andromeda spiral M 31, tilted toward our line of sight. Plate VIII is a photograph of the great Ursa Major spiral M 101, viewed practically along its axis of rotation.

For all views of distinct spiral galaxies give a strong impression of rotation. Thus the M 101 spiral seems to be rotating counterclockwise, dragging the arms behind in a winding-up operation. This rotation we know is real, as shown by detailed studies of actual motions, first by microscopic

measurements of shifts on photographic plates exposed decades apart, and then by spectrum shifts due to line-of-sight
motions. The core of the spiral rotates faster, the arms slower,
in entire accord with gravitational theory. A good picture of
what happens can be seen in an ordinary cup of coffee. Just
stir the black coffee into a swift swirl, then quickly add milk
at the center and watch it spread out into a rotating spiral.
Note particularly how fast it changes its shape and structural
details in a single rotation. What takes only seconds here,
shows what must happen in the billions of years of a spiral of
the sky. Conspicuous changes must occur in a single rotation
of the cosmic swirl. The core rotates faster, while the outward streaming disc loses speed and takes longer to get around,
so being left behind more and more at increased distances
from the core.

### Our Own Milky Way

When we look up at the Milky Way with the naked eye, it
seems to be only a hazy cloud of pearly mist, which is just
what it was thought to be until Galileo reported in 1610
what his telescope had revealed. "The next object which I
observed is the essence or substance of the Milky Way. By the
aid of a telescope anyone can behold this in a manner which so
distinctly appeals to the senses that all disputes which have
tormented philosophers through so many ages are exploded
at once by the irrefragable evidence of our eyes, and we are
freed from wordy disputes upon this subject, for the Galaxy
is nothing else but a mass of innumerable stars planted together in clusters. Upon whatever part of it you direct the
telescope, straightway a vast crowd of stars presents itself to
view; many of them are tolerably large and extremely bright,

but the number of small ones is quite beyond determination."

In short, Galileo proved the Milky Way to be composed of myriads of faint stars concentrated in a misty irregular band encircling the entire sky. But it took a long time to realize that this meant that the Milky Way was really a flattened disclike star cloud. For only in 1750 did the English physician Thomas Wright surmise this, if we understand correctly his

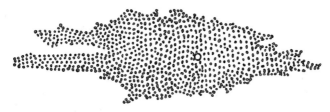

*Figure 1. Herschel's Idea of the Milky Way*

William Herschel pictured the Milky Way as a flattened disc of stars split on one side, with the Sun off center. Viewed from the inside, it appears as a band of crowded stars encircling the firmament. Current ideas give it a shape much like Plate VI. (*And There Was Light*, by Rudolph Thiel, Knopf, 1957.)

pompous description. In 1755, the German philosopher Immanuel Kant did describe it clearly as a lens-shaped cloud of stars, a description that was repeated by Johann H. Lambert in 1761. Then in 1785, the great English astronomer Sir William Herschel, using giant telescopes of his own making, confirmed this by a laborious count of star distribution in the sky. He concluded that the Milky Way was like a "grindstone" in shape, its thickness about one-fifth its diameter. Recent research finds the system less thick, and places the Sun and Earth off toward one edge.

The Sun, being just an average star, is surely not more outstanding than any other star speck in this vast array. All the five thousand or so stars we can see with the naked eye are but a minute nearby fraction of the Milky Way's billions, and even the millions we can explore with telescope and photo-

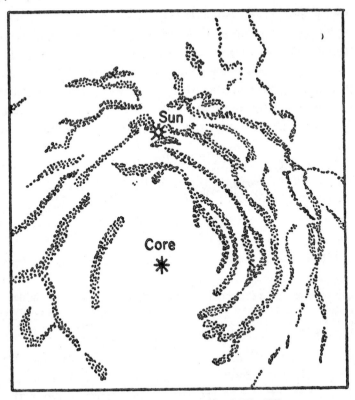

*Figure 2. Spiral Arms of the Milky Way*

An artist's impression derived from a contour map of the distribution of neutral hydrogen based on radio observations of 21cm hydrogen spectrum line at Leiden Observatory, Holland, and Radiophysics Laboratory in Sydney, Australia. (By permission of G. Westerhout.)

graphic plate comprise only a small section of one spiral arm. Lately, however, our radio astronomers have taken a big step in mapping the Milky Way as a whole. Clouds of hydrogen in the spiral arms transmit radio waves about eight inches long, and their movements, directions, and even distances are shown by the spectrum shifts of these waves. Nearby portions of five arms have been thus traced: an innermost unnamed arm is about 15,000 light years from the still mysterious Milky Way core; next is the so-called Sagittarius arm about 21,000 light years from the center; then our own Orion arm, with our Sun near its inner edge and containing the stars and clouds our telescope-cameras reveal, is 27,000 light years from the galactic center; beyond this is the Perseus arm about 34,000 light years out from the center; and finally another unnamed arm is some 40,000 light years out.

Figure 2 is a rather rough map of the Milky Way according to G. Westerhout based on radio observations at the Leiden Observatory in Holland for the Northern Hemisphere (shown to the right) and the Radiophysics Laboratory of Sydney, Australia, for the Southern (shown to the left). Actually it shows only the distribution of neutral hydrogen gas, but is probably a rather fair picture of the spiral arms of our Galaxy, the only parts which contain this gas. Missing from the picture, however, is the huge crowded central core because it lacks such hydrogen gas, and also those farther portions of the arms obscured behind that core. Nevertheless, enough is thus shown to indicate convincingly that our Milky Way has an obviously spiraled structure.

### The Island Universes

As this Milky Way system had thus the rough shape of the spiral galaxies as seen by the improving telescopes of his day, Kant guessed that they too were milky-way systems, and described them as "Island Universes," a name which finds more and more favor with us as we get better acquainted with these remoter systems. However, even Herschel's great telescopes, despite their sizes and powers, were never able to resolve these exterior systems into individual stars. For that, photography had to be developed and applied through giant telescopes moved by high-precision clockwork to follow the stars and so permit exposures of many hours. Even then, the feat of resolving the spirals into individual stars was accomplished only for some of the nearer galaxy neighbors, and only in parts of these. But meanwhile the spectroscope had really settled the question of their composition, for it showed that most of the light from these systems was true starlight, not coming from gas and dust clouds. Not that such gas and dust clouds are lacking, for we do find them in both the Milky Way and other galaxies. However, in the galaxies we find them only in the arms of spirals, causing the blotting out of stars behind them, and most conspicuous when they form the dark obscuring band marking the edge of the equator of rotation when a spiral is seen edgewise. No such gas and dust clouds are found in the central cores of spirals, nor anywhere in the so-called elliptic galaxies.

Such lack of gas and dust clouds, except in the arms of spirals, has the look of something significant, even if we are not quite sure in what way. For why should the elliptic galaxies, and the central cores of spirals, have no such clouds? Perhaps a recent idea by Walter Baade and Lyman Spitzer of Mount Wilson and Palomar Observatories provides part of the answer. They suggest that galaxies occasionally collide, and when they do, their gas and dust clouds meet violently, raising cloud temperatures to points at which they evaporate and dissipate from their galaxies. Elliptic galaxies would then be spirals after collision and removal of the gas-dust clouds. In that case, we would expect more frequent collisions in the more crowded centers of the great clusters of galaxies, as in the constellation Virgo, and should therefore find a greater proportion of elliptic to spiral galaxies than at the outskirts of the cluster. And this is actually what we do find.

### Colliding Galaxies

Moreover, we actually see what appears to be such collisions going on. Plate X is a photograph of NGC 5128, apparently a spiral colliding with a spherical galaxy, from which encounter we may expect the spiral to emerge cleansed of its gas and dust clouds.

This and other observed colliding galaxies have another marked feature; they are the very strongest transmitters of cosmic radio waves, which we are now able to detect with our great new radio telescopes. These "telescopes" should perhaps be better called radio ears—they are really huge bowllike or other highly sensitive directional radio antennae, with which we are now opening up an entirely new and quite promising science, radio astronomy. So far the most powerful radio waves detected come from two colliding galaxies in the con- stellation Cygnus.

Why colliding galaxies should generate such powerful radio waves is fairly well understood since it merely requires a cloud of gas stirred up violently enough, as would certainly happen in such a collision. Of course the resulting broadcast to the Universe can scarcely be called the "harmony of the spheres," being actually radio static. But if its quality is not high, at least its power is, for, as befits the proportions of its potential audience, it has a power twenty billion billion billion times as strong as our most powerful broadcasting stations.

However, we may be quite sure that what we are hearing is not the clashing conflict of giants as huge star masses crash together, for quite certainly the stars of the two galaxies do not themselves collide. If they did, we would see the brilliant explosive disruptions of the meeting masses. Such mutual avoidance seems quite a miracle until we realize that the stars are actually much too far apart for collisions to be at all likely. It is true that to our eyes, and even our telescope-cameras, the galaxy stars seem to merge into apparently continuous clouds of light. But that is due to several factors, such as our earthly atmosphere which spreads out and mixes up the star points until they overlap and merge, plus the graininess in both the retinas of our eyes and the emulsions of our photographic plates, etc. So appearance is quite deceiving and the stars, even in the most crowded parts of the sky, are far apart indeed. Thus our own Sun, one of the myriads that make up a crowded arm in a typical galaxy, has no neighbor star nearer than four and a third light years away, which amounts to roughly twenty-five million times a million miles. And that turns out to be quite average for the spacing of the stars in a galaxy. So the galaxies themselves may occasionally collide, but the individual stars are most unlikely to meet head on and flash out into hot bright exploding vapors. Instead we may say that the stars of two colliding galaxies simply "interpenetrate" through the vast spaces between them.

As to gas and dust clouds, they spread out more continuously to fill up much of those spaces, and are therefore much more likely to meet, with certainly dire results. Those results are probably not merely heating up and dissipating. For as the stars of the interpenetrating galaxies rush through, there are probably what we may call gravitational winds stirring up the cloud masses, carrying much of them along as gravitational captives, and certainly inducing disruptive motions within them, all quite beyond adequate description by either our words or our imaginings.

### Clouds and Stars

However, galaxy collisions do not explain the lack of gas and dust clouds in the core of a spiral which still retains such clouds in its arms. For that we must turn to a peculiarity in the behavior of such clouds of gas and dust. Larger lumps of matter in all sizes up to planets and stars travel in separate orbits about the controlling gravitational center of the particular system, those near the center at higher speeds, those farther away at lesser speeds. But clouds of gas and dust probably do not behave quite that way. Their particles are of course subject to the same gravitational controls, but because of the collisions between the gas molecules and the dust particles, there is a constant transmission and equalizing of speed energies going on. This means that the whole cloud has some tendency to move as a unit, the outer portions being swept along by the inner portions, the outer portions retarding the inner portions. The net result is an increase in centrifugal force in the outer portions, tending to spread the cloud outward. But as the outer portions move into wider orbits which are farther around, they fall a bit behind, and we get the shapes and coiling rotations we observe in the arms of spiral galaxies. It means also that all cloud masses in a galaxy tend to move outward into a centrifugal disc, leaving the core more and more free of such clouds.

Furthermore, such clouds are undoubtedly the raw materials from which stars condense, and in the galaxy core, where the stars are most crowded, we may well assume that the process of star-making is further along, indeed quite completed because the gas and dust material is all dissipated or otherwise used up. Here we should note that any star will keep growing as long as there is any residue of raw material to sweep up and add to its mass by gravitational attraction. We should in fact think of each star as a powerful gravitational center plowing through gas, dust, and other unassorted rubbish in its way, drawing in what matter it can and leaving behind a temporarily cleaned-out tunnel in its wake.

Some of the matter being thus drawn starward will fall point blank right into the star. Much, however, will miss the target, but be captured by its gravitation and start orbiting about it in more or less elliptical paths. About our own Sun, for example, we find just such orbiting matter in the form of comets and meteor swarms. And during a total solar eclipse we see a pearly crown of light, the solar corona, extending far out and perhaps representing the illuminated and highly heated infall of matter being drawn from the thin clouds of interstellar matter and concentrating in density and visibility as it approaches the Sun. Complicating things, when its particles of dust come within a suitable range of minuteness, they are caught up by the pressure of the Sun's outward streaming light and driven away at high speeds. And most certainly there are powerful magnetic forces at work, for the corona shape is strongly rayed. We really know very little about what it is and what causes and shapes it. For the present at least it is a great puzzle, its proper name perhaps just "turmoil."

From all this we might well have anticipated a recent observational discovery by Walter Baade, that the cloudless elliptic galaxies and cores of spirals have only old stars, while the arms of spirals have both old and young stars. The young stars are very distinctive, being brilliant blue giants, apparently still growing vigorously by feeding on the abundant diet of gas, dust, and rubbish still plentiful in the spiral arms. Perhaps many are not really young stars, but old stars rejuvenated in growth and brilliance by a recent dash through a stretch of rich cloud on which to feed. But be they new or only rejuvenated, they do attest to the manner in which stars are born and grow by condensing from nebular masses. How the stars then live on and grow old, we will take up in the next chapter.

Science is doing fairly well, it would seem, in explaining many of the observed facts about the myriads of galaxies which make up the Universe. But there still remain mysteries. One such is the occasional occurrence of so-called "barred spirals," such as the one illustrated in Plate VII. In these the core stretches out on opposite sides to form a long "bar," at the ends of which appear the coiling arms. Frankly, we do not yet understand why this form occurs.

### The Celestial Hierarchy

Reviewing our picture of the Universe which we can observe, and of its story which we must infer, we see a general process of gravitational congregating going on. Whether we begin with the Big Bang, or assume a Steady-State Universe, the matter making it up is being slowly aggregated into separate units, of smaller and smaller sizes, into what Gamow calls a "Hierarchy of Condensations."

First come the great clusters of galaxies, from the rich Virgo and Como clusters, each with its thousand members, down to small ones comparable to our own Local Group with nineteen (at this writing) known members, including of course our own Milky Way system. These, we have noted, may actually be parts of an even greater super-cluster, though that is still debatable.

Then come the individual galaxies, large and small, each composed of myriads of stars, and most of them two-armed spirals obviously rotating. These arms contain clouds of gas and dust. As we live within such a spiral arm, we get many close-up views of those cloud nebulae. They are normally cold and dark, often obscuring the stars behind them, and therefore looking like black holes in the field of stars (Plate XII). Some very small dark specks may be the cloud nuclei just beginning to condense into individual stars, destined to eventual heating by contraction until they glow as new stars. Not all cosmic clouds are dark, however, for here and there we see them illuminated by bright neighbor or contained stars. Such is the great Orion Nebula (visible mistily to the naked eye) shown in Plate IX as photographed. Such nebulae are normally not self-illuminated, as we know from spectroscopic analysis of the light, which proves to be reflected starlight. An interesting confirmation is the unusual nebula depicted in Plate XIII, which is variable, probably because the star which illuminates it is variable, though the variations seem oddly unconnected.

Next downward in the hierarchy of condensations, but not heretofore mentioned, are the globular clusters, spherical and compact clusters of thousands of stars (Plate XIV). About a hundred such clusters attend our Milky Way, being scattered spherically in the space about it, with their center corresponding to that of its core. The telescope readily shows individual stars, at least the outer ones, and there are no indications of gas or dust clouds. These are apparently well organized systems, with the individual stars in each cluster probably revolving in orbits about a common gravitational center. However, the gravitational relations within each cluster must be much too complex for even modern mathematical analysis, as it seems likely that each star follows a highly variable orbit, controlled in the main by the major gravitational center of the cluster as a whole, but being irregularly perturbed by every closely passing star. One would expect frequent collisions and flaring smashups, but despite the appearance of close packing, the stars are actually so far apart that they miss and pass. How the irregular and hectic changes affect the career of a star in a globular cluster we do not know, but it seems quite impossible that any attendant planets could long persist in stable orbits in view of the constant gravitational perturbations by the many shifting relations to the ever passing stars.

Among the stars of the Milky Way proper are many gathered in smaller and irregular clusters of a few stars, the Pleiades (Plate XV) being a typical example. The stars of a given cluster are often much alike (though varying in size), as if they were of one brood, and follow closely parallel paths at much the same speed. Eventually, however, they will probably become more widely scattered by differences in motion, the cluster being only slightly held together by weak gravitational force.

More coherent are the multiple-star groups, two or more stars revolving about each other as gravitationally controlled systems. There are many such, for it is believed that one-quarter of all stars are at least binary (two-star) systems, and perhaps a tenth as many actually multiple. That excludes all merely optical doubles resulting from two unconnected stars being lined up apparently close together as we happen to view them. True binaries are sometimes visual and can be observed revolving about each other, but they must then be near enough to us, and far enough apart from each other, for their separation by the eye and telescope. Others reveal themselves by perfectly periodical light variations due to their eclipsing each other as they revolve. Still others are detected by the spectroscope showing periodical line shifts as the revolving pair move in their orbits alternately from and toward us. Often, by combining such information, we can get very exact knowledge of the actual sizes of the pair, their distance apart, and orbital

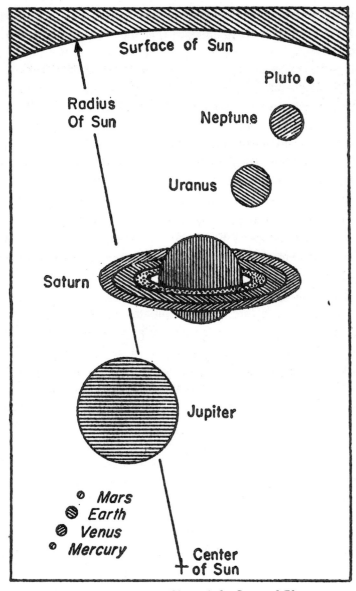

Figure 3. Comparative Sizes of the Sun and Planets

velocities, and from these their actual masses, etc. Then they prove very useful as type samples for the detailed study of all the stars.

Individual stars of course come next in the hierarchy of mass aggregations, and after them the planets and their satellites, together with the whole motley company of asteroids, comets, meteors, etc., which make up the solar systems, our own and all possible others. These members of our own system we can and will study more closely, the Sun for what it tells of stars in general and for its influence on the planets and their life, and those planets and their satellites for what they tell us more directly of themselves.

Summed up, this chapter then tells us how, out of original chaos, order in motion and form evolve by slow natural process, governed dominantly by gravitation.

# CHAPTER 3

## LET THERE BE LIGHT

As our Sun is a star, and a rather typical one at that, it would seem most logical to base our study of the evolution of the stars in general on what we can observe of the Sun. The other stars are so exceedingly far away that they appear as mere points of light, none showing even a visible disc, and therefore none of the close-up details we can see and study on the surface of and nearby the Sun. We can be quite sure that the other stars have fairly similar surfaces and nearby features, and were our purpose merely to picture the close-up appearances of the stars, our Sun model would be very suggestive. On each star we would expect to find a hot bright surface, granulated in appearance because in constant seething turmoil, marked from time to time by huge cyclonic storms which we call sunspots because they appear darker as we look down into their swirling depths. Over the light-giving surface (photosphere) would hover a haze of atmosphere some thousands of miles thick, named the chromosphere because its component chemical elements absorb characteristic wave lengths (colors) of light, and so earmark the light spectrum with lines which tell us what those elements are. The spectra of the stars are also thus marked, but often differently, indicating that there are real differences in their atmospheric compositions and conditions. But at least in those most like our Sun, we would expect that from the atmosphere would shoot great red hydrogen eruptions at speeds up to two hundred miles per second. And enveloping the whole star would be a wide-spreading sheen of pearly mist we call the corona (Latin for crown), best seen during total solar eclipses, and now being studied most revealingly by radio astronomy. (Plate XI) This corona is so shaped and rayed that we surmise very properly that the star is surrounded by a powerful magnetic field, the effects of which we note even here on Earth by magnetic disturbances of our compass needles, by displays of aurora mostly high in our polar skies, and by serious upsets in our radio transmissions, all more marked when the sunspots are more active and the corona takes on certain distinctive shapes. (Plate XVI)

But unfortunately all these observable solar details tell us very little about the real story of the Sun and the stars. We could sum up their meanings by saying that they represent the "boilings" of the surface only, while underneath within the deep interior are going on processes which produce the heat for boiling and determine the more basic changes in the aging of the Sun, and of course the other stars.

### Probing a Star's Interior

Into that interior we obviously cannot go. Even at the surface the temperature is nearly 11,000° F., hot enough to evaporate our Earth and ourselves into elemental gases. And beneath the surface it must be hotter still. But note that though we cannot "go" into that interior, we can nevertheless "penetrate" it for information. In fact, we just did, when we inferred that it must be "hotter still." Of course we penetrate that interior only mentally, but we do it scientifically, applying precise mathematics and exact laws of the behavior of matter learned from our laboratory experiments. But you should be warned that the task is by no means easy, and that it has taken a lot of work just to learn how to do it at all. So we will not attempt to do the actual study, but merely give as clear an account as we can of what is involved, how the job was tackled, and the significant results to date.

We do have some basic facts to go on, though they seem hopelessly scant. We know the Sun's size, its mass, its surface temperature, and the rate at which it is radiating its heat, light, and other energies out into space. And that is about all. Its diameter and its distance we measure the land survey-or's way by delicate triangulation. The diameter turns out to be 864,400 miles, nearly 110 times that of the Earth. From that we can figure its volume, roughly 1,300,000 times that of the Earth. Its mass is known from the speeds and distances at which it swings its several planet dancing-partners about in their orbits. The answer always comes out that the Sun has a mass about 332,000 times that of the Earth. Finally we compare the relative volumes and masses, and note that the Sun has an average density only a quarter that of the Earth. Compared with water density, the figures are: Sun, 1.4 to 1; Earth, 5.5 to 1.

The Sun's surface temperature is about 5750° Absolute, measuring in Centigrade degrees from the true zero of no temperature whatever. The output of radiant energy (mostly heat and light) is accurately known, but hard to express in familiar terms. You can get a good idea, however, from this fact: There is enough heat to melt a shell of ice thirty-six feet thick over the whole surface of the Sun in just one minute. At any rate such are the few facts we have to guide us in our exploring of the interior of the Sun, our prototype for the other stars.

The first attempt at such mental exploring of the Sun's interior was by J. Homer Lane of Washington in 1870. He gave us a fundamental formula for figuring the temperatures and pressures which must prevail at various depths in the interior so that the gas at each depth should have the temperature required to give the expansive power needed for supporting the weight of the overlying masses. In short, gas expansion pressure must always balance the overlying mass pressure or weight. He of course took the simplest possible case, in which all the matter of the Sun (or star) acted as a "perfect" gas of uniform chemical composition throughout. Such a case probably never exists, but what actual variations do occur has proved a most difficult problem. By 1930, several great mathematical physicists had worked out solutions, but arrived at differing answers. Thus Arthur S. Eddington of Cambridge University got a central temperature for the Sun of the order of ten million degrees Absolute, while Edward A. Milne of Oxford University got a temperature several times higher. While Eddington decided that matter at the center behaved as a gas, Sir James H. Jeans of Cambridge concluded that it behaved as a liquid.

The great classic of this period was Eddington's *The Internal Constitution of the Stars* (1926). At least it made clear how involved the whole problem really was. To solve it demanded not just the determination of central pressure and temperature, but the working out of the gradations of pressures and temperatures all the way from center to surface. And this had to be done by trial and error, not just once, but again and again, starting with some arbitrary assumed central temperature (and the known 5750° Absolute at the surface), then laboriously computing the gradations in between. If this turned out wrong, there was nothing to do but try again with a corrected central temperature, and to repeat again and again, getting ever closer to the setup that would mean perfect balancing of inward and outward pressures throughout.

But still there was something vital missing, and Eddington's results were thrown off by lack of two items of knowledge we have since gained. For one thing, he shared the then common belief that the Sun was composed of the various chemical elements in about the same proportions as here on Earth. However, he realized this possible source of error, and gave his results subject to the reservation "that there is not an excessive proportion of hydrogen." Now we know that his reservation was well taken, for the Sun is in fact predominantly composed of hydrogen, and that does indeed make a serious difference.

Second, we have since learned about the real sources of Sun and star energies, and that too makes a big difference. Eddington was indeed far-seeing when he decided that source to be the "annihilation of matter," which is at least partially true. But he did not yet know how that mass-energy conversion was accomplished. So that also hampered him, not only in his study of the star interiors, but in following the evolution of such interiors, and of the stars as we outwardly observe them. For the life histories of the stars (and our Sun), both past and present, do indeed depend on the ways in which they derive the energies they pour out so prodigiously. And our basic problem turns out to be that of learning the sources of the stellar energies.

### What Heats the Stars?

The ancient idea was inevitably that the Sun was merely a globe of burning matter, with little thought given to how long its fuel supply would last. But burning, in those days, was not really understood, and became clear only after Joseph Priestley discovered oxygen in 1774 and Antoine Lavoisier explained combustion in 1775 as the release of heat by the chemical combining of oxygen with carbon (or other elements). That called attention to the fuel supply required, and it was soon realized that the material of the Sun would all burn out in a few thousand years at most. And by this time the geologists, studying the Earth's past, its processes, and its record of changing life, were demanding literally a thousandfold that much time.

Soon too, a new idea was to dominate thinking about the origin of the Sun and planets, the idea that they condensed by gravitational attraction from the diffuse matter of a nebular cloud of gas and dust. As a result, in 1854 the German physicist Hermann von Helmholtz advanced the theory that gradual contraction of the solar mass would convert its potential energy (by falling inward) into kinetic (active) energy of heat and light. He even worked it out in mathematical detail, showing that at its present rate of energy release, the Sun could last for many millions of years. The Englishman Lord Kelvin (William Thomson) later estimated this life-span of the Sun at twenty million years. However, for some stars, Antares for example, the radiation rate is about ten thousand times as high, and gravitational attraction would supply the needed heat for only a few thousand years. But on the other hand, Antares and the other giant red stars were thought to be in a transitory early stage of evolution, and in a short time would settle down (by gravitational contracting) into more ordinary stars, of which the long-lived Sun is a typical example. The general theory went like this:

Once an over-all condensation of a galaxy (of roughly Milky Way proportions) had been brought under gravitational control, lesser local condensations become possible within it, and we think that we actually do see such lesser condensations now occurring as small dark blobs against the bright background of the Milky Way. And such minor concentrations, not too large, can in due time become separate stars, or clusters of stars, settling down into great globes of denser gas, dust, and larger particles. Naturally, gravitation will continuously tend to draw such a globe together, causing it to contract. But this would increase the density and raise the temperature, thereby increasing the expansive force of the gases to resist further contraction. At some size of the star, however, a balance between the opposing forces would stop the star's shrinkage, at least for the time being. Further contraction would then be possible only as energy was lost by radiation into space, thereby cooling the star and reducing the gas expansive force. Further contraction would then raise the temperature somewhat, but at a greater density level, with a somewhat smaller diameter. Actually the star would shrink in size, not intermittently as described above, but gradually, with the opposing forces of contraction and expansion slowly changing but always kept in balance.

Originally, the raw material of the star would be cool gas, dust, and small rubbish, and therefore not luminous. But as it contracted, its temperature would rise, gravitational energy converting into heat energy. Even while still a globe of merely gaseous density (indeed of nearly vacuum density) it would begin to glow, at first only red-hot and not too brightly. But in due course the glow would brighten, and that glow over a huge bulk and concentrated by distance into a mere pin point of light, becomes a really brilliant star to our eyes. The Red Giants, Antares and Betelgeuse for example, seem to be at this stage. Then as contraction went on, the star would slowly get smaller, denser, hotter, and brighter, becoming in turn a yellow star like our Sun, and eventually a white-hot, or even blue-white-hot star like Sirius or Rigel. And so everything seemed to be explained.

But complications appeared, and again the geologists were the troublemakers. First of all they were still demanding even more time than the contraction theory allowed. In fact, they eventually wanted at least a hundred times as much time. For they dug up disturbing evidence that the Earth, and undoubtedly the Sun, had been in existence for billions of years. They also learned that the average temperature of the Earth, as shown by the fossil record of its ancient life, had remained substantially unchanged for at least a billion years, with relatively slight variations up and down. This necessarily means that the Sun too must have been radiating its heat and light without substantial change during all that long period. But the Sun's rate of energy output, if derived only from contraction, can be readily figured by the physicists, and does not fit in at all with these two undoubted facts. First, as we have noted, this source of heat would not have lasted anywhere near a billion years, so our Sun should have long ago been dead and dark. Second, during its life, if heated by contraction alone, it would have doubled its radiation output about every ten million years before finally giving out altogether. So even on the basis of the Sun's present radiation, and going back only ten million years, that radiation should have been only one-half, and the resulting average surface temperature of the Earth should have been below zero Fahrenheit. And a hundred million years ago, when we know that the Earth's climates were actually widely tropical, the figured temperature should have been about 300° below zero F.

### Converting Matter to Energy

It thus became clear that while contraction may well have supplied some of the abundant energy poured out by the Sun and stars, it was certainly not enough. So through the early decades of our century, scientists were looking for some more ample and steady source of solar and stellar energy. They considered longingly the idea that the energy comes from the radioactive breakdown of thorium, uranium, and other unstable heavy elements, but realized that though this might also play a part, it was quite insufficient by itself, largely because these elements were simply not abundant enough. That was why Eddington and others turned to the "annihilation of matter" as the source of star energies.

Eddington actually considered two possibilities. One was the total annihilation of a given bit of matter, the other a partial annihilation incident to a transmuting from one element to another. The first he explained thus: "The ultimate constituents of matter are minute positive charges and negative charges which we can picture as centres of opposite kinds of strain in the ether. If these could be persuaded to run together they would cancel out, leaving nothing but a splash in the ether which spreads out as an electromagnetic wave carrying off the energy released by the undoing of the strain. The amount of this energy is amazingly large; by annihilating a single drop of water we should be supplied with 200 horse-power for a year." He added, "We do not yet know whether it can occur naturally or not. . . . We turn covetous eyes on this store without, however, entertaining much hope of ever discovering the secret of releasing it. If it should prove that the stars have discovered the secret and are using this store to maintain their heat, our prospect of ultimate success would seem distinctly nearer."

He also considered that stellar energies might be released by a partial annihilation of mass in transmuting the elements, particularly hydrogen into helium. He explained (compare our Chapter 1) that the building up of one helium atom out of four hydrogen atoms does in fact involve a slight loss of mass (one part in 139), and that this mass is converted into radiant energy. He also pointed out that the further building up of elements heavier than helium did not convert any comparable mass into energy and could not be counted on as an important source of stellar energies. So he did consider the transmuting of hydrogen into helium as a possible source of energies within the interiors of stars, and even defended that possibility when critics objected that the interiors of stars are not hot enough to induce such transmutations, by retorting that they "go and find a hotter place."

As we know, he had himself already demonstrated that the star interiors are actually hot enough. For in his pioneer study of their internal structure, he had shown that central temperatures must be in the millions of degrees to provide gas expansive forces powerful enough to support the overlying masses and so prevent collapse of the whole gaseous globe. Nevertheless he did lean toward gradual, but total, annihilation of mass as the probable source of stellar energies, rather than merely fractional annihilations in transmutations. But he considered the evidence "not very coherent" and put off the final decision. Also he freely admitted that, in either case, the way in which the energy release was brought about was still an utter mystery.

But the mystery was soon to be solved. In 1927, at Göt-

Plate I. GREAT SPIRAL IN ANDROMEDA. M 31. NGC 224. Nearest spiral galaxy seen at ngle. It is same size as Milky Way. Dimly visible to naked eye, here photographed hrough field of nearby Milky Way stars. Shows small companion spirals NGC 205 and 21. (Mount Wilson and Palomar Observatories.)

*Plate II.* Large and Small Magellanic Clouds. Very nearest exterior galaxies, perhap detached parts of Milky Way. Visible as cloudy patches to naked eye. (Harvard Colleg Observatory.)

*Plate III.* Sombrero Spiral in Virgo. M 104. NGC 4594. Seen edge-on, this swirlir disc of stars appears spindle shaped. Dark belt is obscuring dust thrown out at its edge The strange crossed spot is merely an instrumental effect on the bright image of a near star. (Mount Wilson and Palomar Observatories.)

*Plate IV.* GREAT TRIANGULUM SPIRAL. M 33. NGC 598. Second nearest spiral galaxy, seen full-face. Measurement of shifts of bright patches indicates rotation period of 160,000 years. (Mount Wilson and Palomar Observatories.)

Virgo Cluster.
22 million light years.
750 miles per second.

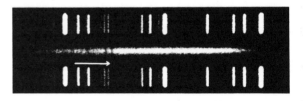

Ursa Major Cluster.
25 million light years.
9300 miles per second.

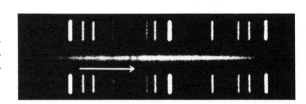

Corona Borealis Cluster.
390 million light years.
13400 miles per second.

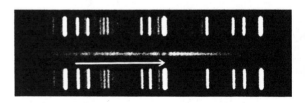

Bootes Cluster.
685 million light years.
24400 miles per second.

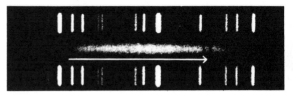

Hydra Cluster.
1100 million light years.
38000 miles per second.

*Plate* V. RED-SHIFTS OF EXTRAGALACTIC NEBULAE. These spectra of cluster nebulae show relation between distance (in light years) and red-shifts (indicating speeds of recession in miles per second). Arrows show amounts of shifts of calcium H and K lines relative to standard spectra alongside. (Mount Wilson and Palomar Observatories.)

tingen University, Houtermans and Atkinson suggested that solar energy was due to the fusion of lightweight atoms, and Houtermans, by 1932, pointed out that neutrons could be used to release the powerful energies dormant in matter. By 1938, a detailed process of solar energy release was discovered independently and almost simultaneously by Carl F. von Weizsäcker of Germany and Hans Bethe of the United States. And about the same time a useful rival process was added by the young American physicist Charles L. Critchfield. And in recent years, other ways of mass-energy conversion have been discovered, one group involving some of the lighter elements, and still another group differing in that helium rather than hydrogen is transmuted into heavier elements, and some of these to still heavier ones.

All these transmuting processes depend upon the penetrating and disrupting of atomic nuclei by collision of high-velocity protons (hydrogen nuclei) or other nuclei. Because of the mutual repulsion caused by their like positive charges, such nuclei are highly resistant to penetration. So the penetrating must be done by the electrically neutral neutrons, or the relative velocities of collision must be so enormous as to overcome the electrical repulsions. Such velocities occur only at temperatures up in the millions of degrees. Then, when they do collide, some nuclei and protons are likely to combine, and so let go a bit of mass to become energy. If the new nucleus is unstable, or disrupted by another collision, a chain of nuclear changes and energy releases may occur, until something stable finally emerges, such as normal helium nuclei. The energy is usually released as gamma rays, readily transformed into heat and light. Or the energy release may be a beta particle or neutrino, which is electrically neutral and extremely lightweight, passing readily through the stellar mass and being quickly lost into outer space, without adding importantly to the interior temperature of the star.

### The Conversion Reactions

Of the more important processes, the simplest is the proton-proton (H-H) reaction of Critchfield, consisting of only three steps, the first being:

$$H' + H' \longrightarrow D^2 \begin{array}{c} \nearrow \text{neutrino} \\ \\ \searrow \\ e^+ + e^- = \text{gamma ray} \end{array}$$

This means that two protons collide and produce one deuteron ($D^2$ or double-weight hydrogen). A neutrino is released and speeds away into space. A positron ($e^+$ or positive charge) is also released, but combines with a free electron ($e^-$ or negative charge), thereby canceling and disappearing as matter, becoming a gamma ray, or bit of active energy.

The second step follows, thus:

$$D^2 + H' \longrightarrow He^3 + \text{gamma ray}$$

which means that the deuteron joins with another proton, releasing a gamma ray and forming an incomplete form of helium ($He^3$).

The completing to ordinary stable helium ($He^4$) may then be accomplished in a number of ways, by far the most common being this:

$$He^3 + He^3 \longrightarrow He^4 + H' + H'$$

in which two incomplete helium nuclei join to form one that is complete, with a couple of protons left over.

In ordinary stars, the other important process is the so-called carbon cycle of Bethe and von Weizsäcker. It is, however, more complex, involving six steps, as follows:

$$C^{12} + H' \longrightarrow N^{13} + \text{gamma ray}$$
$$N^{13} \longrightarrow C^{13} + e^+ + \text{neutrino}$$
$$C^{13} + H' \longrightarrow N^{14} + \text{gamma ray}$$
$$N^{14} + H' \longrightarrow O^{15} + \text{gamma ray}$$
$$O^{15} \longrightarrow N^{15} + e^+ + \text{neutrino}$$
$$N^{15} + H' \longrightarrow C^{12} + He^4$$

This cycle starts with an ordinary carbon nucleus ($C^{12}$). By collision and adding four protons (one at a time), a series of nitrogen, carbon, and oxygen nuclei (some stable, others unstable) are built up, with a final breakup into a helium nucleus ($He^4$) and again a normal carbon nucleus as at the start. The net result is the joining of four hydrogen protons into one helium nucleus, and a release of energy in several stages. The carbon must be there for the process to work, but it is not consumed, and can therefore do its part again and again. More important, throughout the cycle, energy is released in the form of neutrinos which immediately escape, direct gamma rays, and positrons which cancel with electrons to form more gamma rays.

Of less certain importance are a series of mass-energy conversions which result from the joining of protons with some light elements to form helium. These elements are deuterium, lithium, beryllium, and boron. They may take minor parts in energy release in the cooler stages of star development or the cooler portions within ordinary stars. Some of these processes have several steps, but only the over-all reactions are given here:

$$D^2 + H' \longrightarrow He^3$$
$$Li^6 + H' \longrightarrow He^3 + He^4$$
$$Li^7 + H' \longrightarrow 2 He^4$$
$$Be^9 + 2 H' \longrightarrow He^3 + 2 He^4$$
$$B^{10} + 2 H' \longrightarrow 3 He^4$$
$$B^{11} + H' \longrightarrow 3 He^4$$

In this series, the reactions continue only while the supplies of the particular light elements last, the supply of protons (hydrogen nuclei) being presumed to be overabundant.

Again of uncertain importance is the so-called triple-alpha process, as it occurs only rarely and at extremely high temperatures that are seldom, if ever, found in ordinary stars. It differs in that it transmutes helium, rather than hydrogen, into carbon, by these two steps:

$$He^4 + He^4 \longrightarrow Be^8 + \text{gamma ray}$$

$$Be^8 + He^4 \longrightarrow C^{12} + \text{gamma ray}$$

While this reaction transmutes helium into carbon, it may also be followed by further additions of helium nuclei (alpha particles) and transmutations to heavier elements, perhaps up to calcium ($Ca^{40}$). And another reaction, very different from the triple-alpha one, may produce even heavier elements. It needs a supply of $C^{13}$ nuclei (provided by the carbon cycle) and proceeds thus:

$$C^{13} + He^4 \longrightarrow O^{16} + n$$

The important thing is not the production of the oxygen, but of the free neutron (n). This has no electric charge and can therefore invade any atom nucleus and join with it to build up ever heavier elements. Here then we may have the method by which the small supplies of the very heaviest elements may be produced even now, in the interior of at least some greatly overheated stars.


### Reaction Temperatures


Of vital significance in our story of the stars will be the critical temperatures at which these several mass-energy conversions can begin. Thus the deuterium-to-helium reaction can start at somewhat over 500,000°, the lithium-helium reaction at about 2 million degrees, that of beryllium-helium a little above 3 million, and the boron-helium transmutation at a bit under 5 million. Somewhere above that the proton-proton reaction starts and remains dominant up to 15 or more million degrees, when the carbon cycle becomes predominant. The triple-alpha and other reactions transmuting helium or carbon to heavier elements do not occur until temperatures approach 100 million degrees.

Now of course you realize that much of this is pure theory, with only a small basis of experimental fact to go on. The truth is that all the theory is actually highly technical and often seems subtle and uncertain. But in fact it is all rather soundly grounded on basic physical laws experimentally established and mathematically expressed. It will not even do to object that it is impossible to check experimentally or observationally on the million-degree temperatures and transmuting reactions going on within the deep interiors of the Sun and stars, for the fact is that we do have experimental proof. Thus the same theory formulated by Bethe to explain the source of solar energy, also served as the basis for developing the H-bomb, and there we know that the theory really worked.

Furthermore this is the only theory which we have found thus far wholly adequate for explaining the source of stellar energies. So today the carbon cycle and the proton-proton re-action, supplemented somewhat by contraction, are generally accepted by the scientific authorities as the main sources of the agelong outpourings of heat and light by the Sun and other stars. The other reactions involving deuterium, lithium, beryllium, and boron are recognized as probable enough, but relied upon to a lesser degree. The triple-alpha and other proc-esses operating only at approximately 100 million degrees are rarely considered for ordinary stars. As to the Sun itself, the range of its inferred internal temperatures means that both the carbon cycle and the proton-proton reaction are now at work, and that perhaps, some time in the past, the deuterium and related processes played a brief part.

Early in Chapter 2, our quotation from Sir Isaac Newton ended with the words, "And thus might the sun and fixed stars be formed, supposing the matter were of a lucid nature." We now understand that matter becomes lucid in the Sun and stars, initially by gravitational contracting by which the energies of infall convert to the energies of molecular motion we know as heat and light, until temperatures become high enough to start the processes of atomic fusion by which a portion of the matter converts to the abundance of energies by which the stars live on. Thus, by natural process, are accomplished the words, "Let there be light."

It is fairly obvious that our new understanding of the processes of mass-energy conversions must greatly modify both our mental model of a star's interior structure and our ideas of star evolution. Thus we can no longer be satisfied with Eddington's simple model, with its mere gradation of rising temperatures balancing mass pressures as we proceed inward toward the center. Also we realize that the structure must itself change progressively. But that takes us into the evolutionary life histories of the stars, the subject of our next chapter.

# CHAPTER 4

# THE STARS IN THEIR COURSES

In tracing the life history of any star, we may properly assume that at the outset it is composed overwhelmingly of hydrogen, that being in accord with what we know of the proportions of the elements throughout space. Here on Earth we find that the elements heavier than hydrogen and helium are definitely preponderant, but as we shall see, that is probably the result of later and special development. So our star has been slowly condensing from a nebulous mass consisting mostly of gas, some dust, and miscellaneous small rubbish, and settling down about a gravitational center into a globe. Perhaps it also has a slow rotation retaining the momentum of over-all motion in a minor swirl of the original nebulosity.

As it condenses, our incipient star gets hotter and in due time starts to glow, partly because its original heat is packed into less space, partly because the energy of falling is transformed into increased molecular motion, which is heat. This star is packed more densely and has its highest temperatures toward the center, and it is here therefore that mass-energy conversion will presently start, transmuting hydrogen into more and more helium. A helium core therefore forms, growing ever larger. That core remains inert, simply because temperatures are not yet high enough to start the triple-alpha and other processes transmuting its helium into heavier elements.

About this helium core there will be a shell of hydrogen actively transmuting into more helium, and releasing energy in the process. Or perhaps we should speak of several such shells, each dominated by its own temperature range and corresponding transmuting reaction. Thus just outside the helium core, where temperatures are suitably high, the carbon cycle might predominate. Outside that the proton-proton reaction should take over at a somewhat reduced temperature. Then (but perhaps only in the past) should come boron, beryllium, lithium, and deuterium reaction shells, and outside all these another inert shell where temperatures are too low for any mass-energy conversions to occur. If the supply of any of the light elements from boron to deuterium has already been exhausted, its shell must of course have become inert. We do find some lithium and beryllium in the spectrum of the Sun's surface, but we strongly suspect that at the depths of the required 2- or 3-million-degree temperatures, these elements were long ago completely consumed.

## Structure of a Star

If this picture of conditions is correct, it should broadly suggest a proper model of a star's internal structure: (1) a slowly growing core of inert helium; (2) about it a shell (largely hydrogen) actively transmuting into helium and slowly converting a small fraction of its mass into energy, at a rate equal to the outpouring of energy at the stellar surface; and (3) an outer shell (probably mostly hydrogen) too cool for maintaining any mass-energy conversion. However you should be

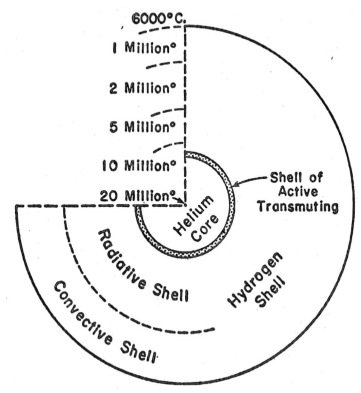

*Figure 4. Internal Structure of the Sun*

From surface to center, density and temperature increase. About the
center is an inert helium core, surrounded by a thin shell of hydrogen
actively transmuting to helium, releasing heat outward through the
inert hydrogen shell, first by radiation, farther out by convection.

warned that the actual picture may not be as simple as this if,
as is often probable, there are internal movements going on
which mix up the matter of the core and shells. Then some
intermixed hydrogen may still be transmuting down to the
very center of the star, to cite just one of many possible
complications.

All in all, at the present time, the general problem of figuring a proper model of a star's interior is getting decidedly more complex. Thus Eddington's classic model of 1926 is quite out of date as much too simple. We will discover, in fact, that it must be replaced, not by one, but several models, differing because of variations in star size, mass, density, composition, age, etc. The most recent attempts at such model-building are summed up by the Princeton astronomer Martin Schwarzschild in his book on the *Structure and Evolution of the Stars* (1958). It may prove to be a classic, belonging in every astronomer's library. Although extremely technical and full of higher mathematics, it is frankly just a preliminary attack on the problem, the author estimating that there are upward of ten thousand man-years of computing work ahead for any conclusive star-model results, quite aside from much related observational research to be done. As to those formidable man-years of computing, our modern high-speed electronic computers are of course being put to work to make short work of them.

Yet some of the detail problems do not seem too difficult. Thus an inert core produces no heat by mass-energy conversion and would tend to become uniform in temperature throughout. Yet it must somehow manage to maintain its pressure balances at all distances from the center. This is done simply by packing its matter more densely toward the center. Such contraction will produce more heat, but this will soon spread throughout the core, which will eventually take on the temperature maintained by the actively transmuting shell of hydrogen around it.

### Mechanism of a Star

But other problems that look easy prove more tricky. Thus how can the energy released near the star's center, or in a deep interior shell, be then transported to the surface? We may assume that ordinary conduction, as through a solid, plays little part because the star's material behaves like a gas. On the other hand, we ordinarily expect a gas (certainly hydrogen) to be transparent, so that transport by radiation (direct travel of the energy-waves) would always be easy. However, largely because of the extreme heat, the atoms are so disrupted and disturbed that they absorb and therefore block radiant energy, thus preventing such effective transport by radiation. That leaves convection as the only possible way of heat transport, whereby hotter expanded fluids (gases and liquids) rise upward while the cooler denser fluids sink downward—a circulation of matter (and its heat) which can be likened to boiling. Within a star, however, even such convective transport is probably unexpectedly slow, with the boiling turmoil relatively slight except at the very surface. Yet somehow the interior heat does travel upward, and finally pours out prodigiously from the surface, and how this can be done becomes a real problem. Also it multiplies the general problem, simply by adding complicating effects. Thus Schwarzschild finds that the method of transport varies with the mass of the star. For the Sun and smaller stars, heat transport is mainly radiative in the core, and convective farther out. In the larger stars the conditions are quite reversed, core transport being convective, the transport from there out radiative.

This makes a very practical difference in our model-making, for the larger stars at least. Because of convection, the helium of the core and the hydrogen about it will be constantly circulating and mixing so as to destroy any definite boundary between them. And because of the presence of hydrogen within the core, mass-energy conversion must still be going on within it. And this is but one of many factors which complicate, in most technical ways, our study of the structures, energy production, and evolution of the stars.

But while we are struggling with the tricky details of star model-making, let us not forget our over-all purpose, which is to trace the story or stories of star evolution, and to find explanations for the variant characteristics of the stars as we observe them in their present states. For the stars do vary, in more ways than meet the eye, and these differences must somehow be explained before we can really know the stars and properly trace their evolutions.

### The Look of the Stars

When we look out upon the starry sky, we note only a few of the pertinent facts about the stars, such as variations in brightness and color, and a few significant groupings into clusters and Milky Way. To these we must now add the multitude of detailed disclosures by telescope, photography, spectroscope, and many other devices employed by the modern astronomer, including a recently developed array of radio instruments now contributing surprisingly to our knowledge of the universe both near and far. Together these disclosures now represent a vast and ever growing, but far from complete, volume of descriptive facts about the universe of stars as they are, and as we must somehow explain them.

The Greek astronomer Hipparchus of the second century B.C. was presumably the first to apply a scale of brightness to the stars. The very brightest he called First Magnitude, for the same reason that we call something "first class." Then he designated the very dimmest stars the eye can see as Sixth Magnitude, grading the stars between by intermediate magnitudes. This, unfortunately, gives a scale in reverse, the low-number magnitudes being brighter, the high-number magnitudes dimmer, which is naturally quite confusing. A better scale would be one giving relative brightness.

Besides that, such differences in apparent brightness (using any scale) are themselves deceptive because of differences in star distances. For we all realize that distance dims, and that we can get no proper idea of the real brightness unless we measure star distances and take them into account. But even today we can measure the distances accurately for only a few nearby stars. However, those nearby few do provide a sampling of star characteristics both useful in itself and providing a basis by which we can fairly estimate even greater distances. As a result we now have a considerable list of stars the actual luminosities of which we can estimate more or less closely, ranging from supergiants tens of thousands times brighter than the Sun, down to dim red dwarfs barely glowing and hardly visible at all.

Color differences, we shall find, are also meaningful in our story. But the naked eye sees only the marked color differences. A few stars, such as Antares, Betelgeuse, and Aldebaran, are clear shades of red or orange. Others, such as Capella, are noticeably yellow. Many are white or blue-white, Sirius and Rigel being outstanding. A few telescopic stars are beautifully green, but only one, Zubeneschamali, brightest in the dim constellation Libra, is naked-eye green, best seen in our midnight sky in early summer.

The spectroscope, however, analyzes and distinguishes color differences more effectively, and has in fact led to our fundamental classification of the stars. After several preliminary attempts at spectrum classification based on visual observation, a systematic program of photographic recording of star spectra was begun in 1885, culminating in the Harvard system of classification. It originally arranged the stars into classes designated by the letters A to Q in alphabetical order. But for various good reasons this has since been modified by dropping several letters, adding a couple, and rearranging the order a bit, the present arrangement being O, B, A, F, G, K, M, R, N, and S. Since this is rather difficult to memorize, astronomers, being only human, cooked up this memory-aid sentence, "Oh be a fine girl, kiss me right now, sweetheart," with some argument as to whether the last word should not be "smooch," "smack," or perhaps "slap."

By now an immense job of gathering and classifying such spectra has been done. This was made easier because it could be done wholesale. By putting a big (but low-power) prism up in front of the telescope-camera, each pinpoint of light from a star was spread out into a line of dots. These could then be photographed as crosslines by moving the telescope slowly crosswise during the exposure. The result was a whole plate full of star spectra with very little work and trouble. Up to date, more than 400,000 star spectra have been thus photographed, classified, and catalogued.

Of course these spectra tell us only of the surface chemistries and conditions of stars, and nothing directly of their interior conditions. So they are less direct help than we might wish, but as they are the best we have, we must do what we can with them. That may actually be a good deal.

Thus one thing important that we can infer from a star spectrum is the surface temperature to which it is evidently due. Typical Absolute temperatures for several classes are: O, 30,000°; B, 20,000°; A, 11,000°; F, 8000°; G, 6000°; K,

4000°; and M, 3000°. These temperatures are of course responsible for the colors from blue-white-hot down to red-hot as seen by the eye. Also they are responsible for the brightness per unit area of a star's surface, the hotter stars being brighter, the cooler ones dimmer. From that we conclude that the total luminosity of a star must depend on such unit brightness multiplied by its surface area.

### Star Mass and Luminosity

Not so obvious is another basic relationship first discovered by Arthur S. Eddington on theoretical grounds and since confirmed by direct observation. This is a rather surprising tie-in between the total luminosity of a star and its mass. Star masses, unfortunately, can be determined accurately for only a few binary stars, but all the known data (except for White Dwarfs) prove Eddington right. And this seems odd because stars vary so much in both size and unit brightness (and therefore temperature), and also in mass and density. The mass-luminosity law really implies that somehow these various features are kept in a working balance, not only in each individual star now, but also throughout its course of evolution. Eddington perspicaciously hit on the theory behind this even before the fact itself was discovered.

### The H-R Diagram

Meaningful facts are not always obvious, but must be revealed by a proper sorting of an apparently mixed-up array of facts. Such a meaningful sorting out of facts was first worked out in 1913 by Henry Norris Russell of Princeton on a graphic chart since known as the H-R diagram. The *H* in its name stands for Ejnar Hertzsprung, the Danish astronomer who had previously done some related work, and the *R* of course for Russell himself. Originally, Russell put the spectral class letters as a row across the bottom from O to M, and the absolute magnitudes as a vertical scale, the brightest at the top. Then he made a dot for each star where the magnitude and spectral class lines intersected. That obviously showed whatever relationship there might be between magnitude and spectral class. The result proved surprisingly suggestive, as we shall soon see.

You will often come across this H-R diagram in writings on astronomy, but you may be confused by the different ways in which its scales are given. That is because it is really very versatile in showing various (but related) meanings of the facts it summarizes. Thus the vertical scale of absolute magnitudes can also be expressed as luminosities compared with our Sun. Or because of the mass-luminosity law, the vertical scale can be one of relative masses. And the horizontal scale of spectral classes (O to M) can be replaced by one of predominant colors (perhaps expressed in wave lengths), or more usually surface temperatures. And you are likely to come across scales expressed in logarithms, say of luminosities or temperatures, these being convenient computing short cuts for the astronomer. All of which adds up to the fact that the H-R diagram is widely useful and revealing, and therefore used for many purposes.

On the H-R diagram, most of the stars fall in a narrow band extending diagonally from the bright blue-white O stars (upper left) down to the dim red-dwarf M stars (lower right,) this being called the Main Sequence. Then down below to the left fall a few dim white stars, the White Dwarfs, very special in several ways. And up above and toward the right is an assortment of odd stars, such as Red Giants, supergiants, and pulsating variables. Our Sun lies in the Main Sequence, which

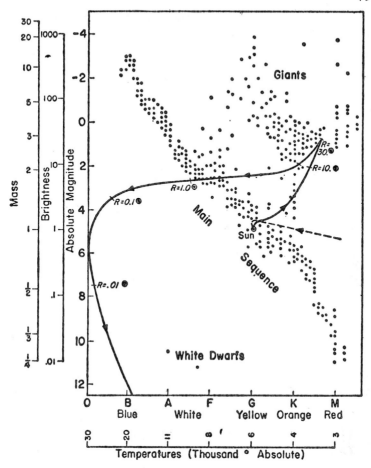

*Figure 5. Career of the Sun on H-R Diagram*

Shows the Sun's present position in Main Sequence. Its past career is shown by a dashed line. Its future career, after lingering in Main Sequence, is described in Chapter 12. (By permission from *Elements of Astronomy*, Fifth Ed., by E. A. Fath. Copyright 1955, McGraw-Hill Book Co., Inc.)

makes it an ordinary star, a bit below and to the right of the midpoint in the sequence, which makes it somewhat below average in surface temperature, luminosity, mass, etc. More specifically, it is a Class G star of absolute magnitude +4.85,

yellowish in color, with a surface temperature of 5750 degrees
(on the Kelvin or Absolute scale).

Half a century ago, astronomical thinking was dominated by
the Helmholtz idea that star energy resulted from gravitational
contraction of its mass, originally condensed from a nebular
cloud of gas and dust. A star evolved, it was thought, by gaseous
condensing and heating from the cool nebula, through a young
Red-Giant stage of low temperature, on to a blue-white-giant
stage of high temperature. Then, becoming increasingly compact, it reached a stage where it could not shrink further, and
would then begin to cool, gradually sinking through middle-
aged yellow down to old red and finally dark dead stages.
Norman Lockyer had given this theory quite definite and
convincing form. Then Hertzsprung in 1905 announced the
distinction between giant and dwarf stars and in 1913 Russell
diagramed in the Main Sequence what seemed to be exactly
the assortment of stars required to enforce this theory. However, the stray stars outside the sequence did make trouble,
being hard to place properly in the whole picture.

And again, a serious hitch turned out to be that contraction
simply could not provide the length of life for Sun and Earth
which the geologists were demanding. And soon the physicists,
exploring the atom and its possibilities, suspected other more
adequate sources of energy by mass annihilation. Eddington,
leaning toward total (but gradual) mass annihilation, began
insisting that a star (after an initial contraction from nebula to
Red Giant to white giant) can move down the Main Sequence
by a slow loss of mass, winding up as a dwarf of low mass,
dense, cool, and dim.

But a score of years ago this basic thinking was all changed
by the discovery of the several sources of stellar energy in the
transmuting reactions (largely of hydrogen to helium) with a

small fraction of mass-energy conversion. In this fresh soil, new ideas on stellar evolution began to sprout. Thus by 1940, Gamow offered two ideas, one about the sequence of reactions, the other changing the direction of star movement along the Main Sequence.

### Early Star Stages

His first contribution was that as the stars condensed from nebulae through the Red-Giant stage, their contraction raised their central temperatures, first high enough for the deuterium-helium reaction to start. This reaction then continued only so long as the deuterium supply lasted, a comparatively brief period, during which high temperatures prevented further contraction. Then at successively higher and higher temperatures, by alternating contraction and mass-energy conversion, the lithium, beryllium, and boron stages would be passed through, with a final contraction raising the temperatures to trigger the proton-proton and carbon-cycle reactions. All the preliminary stages, Gamow thought, would occur in the general area of the Red Giants, off to the upper right in the H-R diagram, the star progressing intermittently toward the left and finally arriving in the Main Sequence with the starting of the proton-proton reaction. Also, while in the early mass-energy conversion stages, some of the stars, Gamow surmised, would run into periods of instability causing them to pulsate as variable stars. Such stars are actually found in this H-R area, representing a special problem which must somehow be explained, either Gamow's way or some other.

Once arrived at the Main Sequence stage, the star would remain there for a very long period until the usable supply of hydrogen gave out, thus explaining the preponderance of these

stars which make this the *main* sequence. Here Gamow added
his second idea, that the star would then move *upward* along
the Main Sequence, by slowly getting hotter and brighter until,
the hydrogen supply finally giving out, the star would start
cooling and contracting again, finally winding up as a White
Dwarf, of such extreme density that its very atoms are crushed
so closely together that a cubic inch of matter weighs a ton
or more. That remarkable condition itself had already been
established and was not original with Gamow. The idea he did
contribute was that the stars move *up* in the Main Sequence
as they slowly evolve, exactly the opposite of previous theories.
However, he did get into a bit of trouble here with the mass-
luminosity law which demands increase in the star's mass as it
increases in luminosity. Gamow did try an explanation, but
the matter is still in dispute.

### Career of a Star

Of course, with growing knowledge of the transmuting
reactions and their energy releases, more and more understanding came to the workers in this very active field. As
summed up, largely following Schwarzschild, the tentative results at the moment are substantially these:

It is agreed that the stars do condense from gas and dust
nebulosities, heating first by slow contraction and arriving
finally at the Main Sequence (from the right). Then rising
temperatures start the proton-proton and carbon-cycle transmuting reactions. Meantime, Gamow's preliminary and inter-
mittent stages of deuterium, lithium, beryllium, and boron
reactions may or may not occur, opinion being divided. But
at least as a possible explanation of the pulsating variable stars,
this idea should be kept in mind.

Once arrived at the Main Sequence, the star remains there for a long period depending upon its original mass, but without significant change in that mass. For it is thought that the star masses differ right from the very start as they condense out of blobs of nebular matter of differing sizes, the amount of matter being quite accidental. Some stars are therefore born small and destined ultimately to become only small red dwarfs. Others start with medium mass, much like our own Sun, and are therefore destined to become only medium stars. Still others begin gigantically, fated to become massive blue-white supergiants. Each will therefore reach the Main Sequence at its own mass and luminosity level, and then remain there with only slight outward change. And that Main Sequence will then be quite continuous from top to bottom, all mass-sizes being represented in a random array.

But such original mass will determine the star's course and speed of evolution. The more massive stars are actually living at a faster pace, using up energy at a higher rate per unit mass, losing their hydrogen reserve more swiftly, and being therefore doomed to survive for a shorter period. Thus a supergiant may run its full Main Sequence course in some hundreds of thousands of years, a blue-white giant in a few million years, while our Sun (below medium in mass) has a total life expectancy of about twelve billion years. The prospect for the small red dwarfs is a practical eternity, but one of utter dullness. Assuming, as we apparently must, that our Milky Way galaxy took form some twelve or thirteen billion years ago, these red dwarfs must all be in their comparative youth, certainly not far enough aged in internal development to move out of the Main Sequence. So we have not yet any advanced samples to show us what their ultimate fate may be, and no one has yet worked out that fate on the basis of theory, unless it be dull dying by mere cooling.

## Our Medium-Mass Sun

We of course take more interest in the fate of the medium-mass stars, our own Sun being such a star, and the future of the Earth and its Life (meaning ourselves), being involved in its destiny. At present the Sun is not far enough along its Main Sequence development for its future to be at all threatening. Its energy sources, at the moment, are largely the proton-proton reaction and the carbon cycle, but so far probably only 6 per cent of its hydrogen supply has been transmuted into the growing helium core. It was at first thought that the carbon cycle predominates in the Sun, but Schwarzschild concludes that the proton-proton reaction is now the more important. As to its future in the Main Sequence, which we translate into its Life Expectancy for our human purposes, it has been estimated at about another six billion years.

During that period an internal aging will be going on. The helium core will keep growing, fed from the hydrogen-transmuting shell about it, with that shell slowly rising toward the surface. The core itself will pack closer and closer, until atom-crushing and superdensities result, much as in the White Dwarfs. Meanwhile, the active shell will get hotter, expand, and lose density, even though the surface temperature may actually decrease. On the H-R diagram, the Sun will move slightly off to the right toward redness, and also upward in luminosity, in other words toward the Red-Giant area. This general tendency will continue until (according to Allan R. Sandage of Mount Wilson and Palomar Observatories) the Sun has used up about 12 per cent of its original hydrogen supply and expanded to four times its present diameter. At this critical point, instability will set in, and the Sun will start to consume its remaining hydrogen supply at an enormous rate and expand rapidly in size until it reaches a diameter some thirty times its present one, equivalent to a volume 27,000 times as great, and extremely low density. Despite the high rate of hydrogen consumption and consequent rise of energy output, it will glow only a dull red, but give off much more heat to the Earth. In other words, it will be a Red Giant, though a rather small one, destined eventually to cool and shrink somehow or other. But what will finally happen is a matter for conjecture, which we will take up in a moment, after considering the probable evolution of the more massive blue-white stars of the Main Sequence.

### The Supergiant Stars

Any such super-massive star, we have already learned, has no distinct helium core in its early stages, but a convectively mixed interior in which hydrogen-transmuting goes on down to the very center. But the hydrogen is still being continuously depleted, and the helium content growing. Also the temperatures, from center to surface, are higher than in smaller stars. One consequence is that the carbon cycle is the dominating transmutation and energy-releasing process. Another is that while the star as a whole is expanding because of rising temperatures, the core, now largely helium, is contracting, and so rising to extremely high temperatures. Then as the core temperature finally approaches 100 million degrees, the triple-alpha and other reactions begin to transmute the helium into carbon and even heavier elements. On the H-R diagram (for reasons too technical and subtle for us to follow) the star will move toward the right, with hesitating retreats to the left, eventually ending up also in the Red-Giant area.

Whether a star comes from the Main Sequence by the medium-mass or giant-mass route, once in the Red-Giant stage its mass may be subject to rapid reduction, on occasion up to perhaps an 85 per cent loss. This loss is not so much by mass-energy conversion as by direct ejection of its matter into space. Several factors may be responsible, one being outward pressure by the star's own light on minute dust particles, another the pressure of sonic (sound) waves in the low-density surface layers, still another just gas dispersion from the surface of the vastly expanded star out where the gravitational grip is greatly weakened by remoteness from the center. The main loss is of course hydrogen, it being most easily dispersed and driven off. This drastically reduces the primary fuel supply, and the duration of the Red-Giant stage is therefore probably brief, with ordinarily a rapid and sharp drop to the White-Dwarf stage of extreme density, reduced volume, and surface area, with low luminosity despite white-hot surface temperatures. In other words, the White Dwarf may be only the dense core of a Red Giant that has lost its rare and red envelope into outer space. As for the future of the White-Dwarf core, we must apparently assume only slow cooling, ending in a death of eternal darkness.

### The Exploding Stars

However, something else may perhaps happen in the later stages of a very few of the more massive stars—an explosive end as a nova or supernova. What brings it about we do not know, though we do assume it is some condition which upsets the balanced state of the star's interior. We have, however, observed the results, fairly often for ordinary novae, more rarely for the supernovae. In each case, a dim star flares up suddenly to a luminosity tens or hundreds of thousand times greater, then more slowly and irregularly fades away to its former dimness. Our spectroscope tells us of matter swiftly approaching us in violent explosive expansion. And for years thereafter, our telescope-cameras may show an ever expanding nebulosity about the star as its substance is being dispersed into space.

The Crab Nebula (M1) in Taurus is a good example (Plate XVII). Its photograph shows a weirdly tangled mass of illuminated gas and dust. Its spectrum reveals a bursting speed toward us of 680 miles per second. Its position is that of the supernova of 1054 A.D., observed by the Chinese and Japanese, and by them politely called the *guest star*. It flared up suddenly to a brightness seen even in daylight and took two years to fade from naked-eye visibility. Judging by its expansion speed, it must now be six or seven light years in diameter, and 3300 light years away. But strangest of all, it is one of the most powerful sources of radio emission. The explanation recently offered by the Soviet astronomer I. S. Shklovsky is that its electrons are speeded up to high velocities about it by a powerful magnetic field as in a modern laboratory synchrotron. Such accelerated electrons should give off polarized light, and photographs through polaroid screens, done first by Soviet astronomer V. A. Dombrovsky and confirmed both in Holland and with the 200-inch Palomar reflector, show just such polarizing.

Another, and seemingly related phenomenon, has recently been discovered by using red-sensitive photographic plates and the proper red filters which let through one particular line of the hydrogen spectrum. They reveal what may be called hydrogen halos or rings. Actually they are not rings at all, but vast thin shells of hydrogen gas visible only near the edges where the light passes through enough depth of gas to take on its color. The most conspicuous of these hydrogen rings appears in the constellation Orion, being somewhat elliptical, and large enough to include all the bright stars of Orion except Rigel and Bellatrix. There are a few similar rings elsewhere in the Milky Way, and one is even known in the Large Magellanic Cloud outside our own Galaxy.

The Orion shell is about three hundred light years in diameter, and it is surmised to be the end result of a supernova explosion several million years ago. The material of the exploding star kept expanding at a speed of perhaps a thousand miles per second, pushing before it whatever interstellar matter it encountered, mostly hydrogen gas. The resistance of this obstructing matter gradually slowed up the explosive speeds until they were reduced to a mere mile or two per second, when the hydrogen gas molecules were able to evade the outward thrusts, and the hydrogen shell reached its maximum extent.

In their systematic scanning of the heavens the radio astronomers have found a few concentrated points of powerful radio emission. These they call "radio stars" even though the telescope-cameras reveal them to be exploding gas and dust clouds such as the Crab Nebula or vast colliding galaxies such as those discussed in Chapter 2. However, no radio star proper was known until the recent announcement from the Radio Observatory of the California Institute of Technology of strong radio signals (ten million times that of our Sun; from a faint telescopic star, 3C-48 in the constellation Triangulum. Spectroscopic studies with the 200-inch reflector at Mount Palomar disclose these facts: a spectrum showing calcium, helium, and oxygen, but strangely lacking in hydrogen, unlike any previously known star; a gaseous cloud surrounding the star; and high-velocity electrons moving in a magnetic field, the resulting synchrotron-like radiation producing both its light and its radio signals. Furthermore, this baffling star may be quite close, as star distances go, to our own Solar System.

Frankly, we are doing much guessing about these last stages and final endings of the star careers. Thus it may well be that within them the heavy elements are formed by higher-temperature transmutations from helium and carbon. Perhaps these rarer elements are then locked up forever in the dense cores of the White Dwarfs destined for ultimate cold dark death. Or perhaps those elements are dispersed into interstellar space by Red Giants ejecting much of their substance, or by novae dissipating such matter by violent explosions. Or are those explosions due to rapid superheating to billions of degrees for a few final seconds, during which the heavier elements are built up and then scattered out into space? This is the contention of Margaret and Geoffrey Burbidge of Yerkes Observatory, who believe that this is the origin of such heavy elements in our Universe, rather than in a fiery early moment in the rapid cooling following the Big Bang. If so, it follows that as the galaxies grow older, the proportion of heavy elements must increase and that younger stars and their planets must contain more such matter. From this, the youth of our Sun compared with the Universe as a whole, and a careful estimate of the relatively high proportion of heavy elements revealed by the Sun's surface spectrum, the Burbidges conclude that our Solar System belongs in what they call the "third generation" in the development of the Universe.

## Is the Universe Running Down?

So far, much of all this is obviously speculative, with only a small basis of factual evidence. Of only these over-all facts are we fairly sure, that the matter of the Universe, congregating into galaxies and the stars within them, attains temperatures within those stars which induce mass-energy conversions, slowly reducing the total amount of mass and increasing the total amount of energy, but meanwhile dissipating that energy wastefully into the space between. It does indeed appear that our Universe is wasting away and running down.

Is there, however, a reverse process going on? Are there, off in space perhaps, meetings of energy units, and conversion somehow back into mass, presumably those protons which capture each its own electron to become the primal hydrogen atoms? Without committing himself to this particular theory, our good dissenter Fred Hoyle seems to think that there is such creation of mass going on continuously, thereby renewing the Universe in mass, and assuring it an eternity of existence and active evolution. Or is this renewal attained by the cycle of the Öpik Oscillating Universe by which all matter (and somehow energy too) is brought together by a Big Collapse ending in a Big Squeeze culminating in a Big Bang starting a new Expanding Universe going through all the processes of congregating into galaxies and stars, with resultant high temperatures causing new mass-energy conversions whereby heavy elements are again built up out of the primal hydrogen to which matter must have been reduced at the moment of maximum squeeze? And so, of course, ad infinitum.

Now you may feel that all this is most interesting, but no practical or urgent concern of yours, you being much more interested in the more mundane origins and conditions of the Earth itself. You will therefore be gratified that now we are about to return back to Earth, to how it was born and then prepared for comfortable habitation by you and me.

# CHAPTER 5

# THE BROOD OF THE SUN

THE questions we ask often reveal the short-comings of our minds. Notably it has been so in the ways mankind has asked about the origin of the World. Thus in ancient and medieval times, it was widely believed that the World was flat, and that over it arched a firmament supporting Sun, Moon, planets, and stars. The problem was therefore how the firmament was separated and elevated above the Earth. One answer, painted on an Egyptian mummy case, depicts the creation god Shu lifting Nuit, the goddess of night, to the sky, having torn her from the arms of her husband Sibu, the Earth god, whose resisting struggles caused the contorted irregularities of the Earth's surface.

Such answers predominated well into the sixteenth century, based on the prevailing popular belief in the World's flatness. Believe it or not, that belief persists here and there to this day, and only a quarter of a century ago, a Flat Earth Society still flourished in London. But by the early 1500s, the Earth had already been circumnavigated by the ships of Magellan and a good start made in its rough mapping and measurement. And of course, even in ancient Greek days, the informed and un-prejudiced considered the flat Earth as nonsense. For at least the scientific-minded, following Pythagoras, realized that the

Earth was a sphere, as shown by the visible curvature of the
surface of the sea, and by the roundness of the shadow cast
by the Earth upon the Moon during every lunar eclipse.
Eratosthenes even succeeded in roughly measuring the Earth's
size by sighting the angular elevations of the Sun at the cities

*Figure 6.  Egyptian Creation of the Firmament*

Creation god Shu tears Nuit, goddess of night, from her husband Sibu,
god of earth, and lifts her up to form the firmament. The original is
painted on a mummy case.

of Alexandria and Syene (present-day Assouan). This gave
him the fraction of the Earth's circumference between them.
He then multiplied accordingly their crudely measured distance apart to get the full circumference, which came out very
close indeed to its actual size.

Yet for some two thousand years, the man in the street
held on to belief in the flatness of the World, and the foolish
questions as to its origin were met by the foolish answers of

tradition. But when the exploring voyages of Columbus, Magellan, and others finally proved that the World was round, even the man in the street was convinced and open to new ideas. Copernicus, in the pages of an upsetting book, revived an old Greek idea, which Galileo later began proving with his telescope, that the Earth was not the center of the Universe, but was just one of a family of planet-worlds circling about the Sun as center. Those planets and the Sun, studied close-up through the telescope, proved to be round and rotating. It was found that the planet Jupiter had an encircling satellite family of its own, and the planet Saturn a strange ring like the flat brim of a hat. The Moon, when magnified, showed a surface full of mountains and volcanic craters, and wide flat areas at first mistaken for seas. So a fairly true picture of our Solar System began emerging, and the problem of its creation took on a new and proper form permitting sensible answers.

### The Universe Ruled by Law

Besides this truer picture of the facts, a profound change in mental attitude developed during the seventeenth century—a recognition that the Universe is governed by physical law. Three men were conspicuously responsible: Galileo, Kepler, and Newton.

Galileo Galilei began the development with a questioning mind that set him to experimenting with falling bodies. He upset an older assumption that heavy objects fall faster than light ones by announcing that all bodies fall at the same rate (unless retarded by air resistance). He proved it by visible demonstration at the leaning tower of Pisa, according to doubtful legend. The rate of fall, he discovered, increases by an equal amount during each second of fall, namely by some thirty-two feet per second.

Johannes Kepler, oddly enough, used a somewhat unscientific approach. He had inherited, as it were, a great mass of precise observations on the apparent movements of the planets in the sky, carefully made by the astronomer Tycho Brahe over a lifetime. Kepler concentrated on the planet Mars because the data on it was the most complete. He had no real idea what its actual movements were, but set about trying out every conceivable scheme, however absurd it might seem, checking each one against the observed positions, and discarding those which did not fit the facts. In the end he did discover the true motion of Mars (and the other planets) and expressed them in three basic laws.

It was perhaps because he was thus willing to try anything once, that Kepler was able (rather reluctantly) to break away from all previous opinion, which held that planets must move in perfect circles just because circles are perfect. For he did find that, in fact, each planet moved in an elliptical orbit, with the Sun at one focus of the ellipse. Second he found that a line joining planet and Sun (the radius vector) sweeps over equal areas in equal times. His third law came later, that the cubes of the planet distances are proportional to the squares of their periods of revolution about the Sun. Be it noted here that Kepler was no real theorist and had no idea why these three laws prevailed, but merely found by trial and error that they did indeed fit the facts of observation.

Sir Isaac Newton, on the other hand, was a profound theorist, who took the laws found by Galileo and Kepler, and from them worked out two basic and simple laws which explained everything. One was the law of inertia, which stated that any mass will continue in a state of rest or uniform motion, unless changed by an outside force. The other was that of gravitation, which stated that the attraction between two masses will vary directly as the product of their masses and inversely as the square of their distances apart, measured from center to center if they are globes. With these two simple laws and the calculus (a new mathematical system which he developed for easier handling of intricate problems), he not only explained Kepler's three laws of planetary motion, but demonstrated that the Universe, in all its parts and movements, is governed by uniform basic laws. Very soon the mathematical astronomers put these laws to every possible test, and finding them always true, applied them in all their thinking, as for example to the problem of the origin of the Sun and its family. They merely assumed that Newton's universal and ever controlling laws must have been in force and effective control when the Solar System was born.

### The Brood Birth

Notice here how their viewpoint had broadened, how they were now thinking how the whole Solar System was born rather than the Earth alone. With the new knowledge and understanding, it was realized that all the planets must have been born together as one brood in a single blessed event. For all the nine planets (and, as we now know, some thousands of asteroids) revolve about the Sun in one direction, the same as the direction of the Sun's rotation, and follow orbits in planes generally near that plane of rotation. Add the fact that, with but one exception, the planets also rotate in this direction and close to that plane. All this suggests that a single event, such as a brood birth, was responsible for this uniformity. Of course we inhabitants of the Earth do regard our own World as of overwhelming importance, but we should also remember that as masses go in the family of the planets, our world is but one part in four hundred, and so quite insignificant weightwise. Therefore our problem, fairly stated, is how the whole planetary family of the Sun was born.

At any rate, by the middle of the eighteenth century new answers began to appear which we can finally call scientific. The first was that of the French naturalist Comte Georges Louis Leclerc de Buffon. In one of the forty-four volumes of his *Natural History*, a brilliant summary of the natural science of his day, he described in 1749 the formation of the planetary system as due to a collision between the Sun and what he called a "comet" rushing in from outer space. This body, which he thought of as very massive, had struck the Sun a glancing blow and knocked off a number of pieces, the blow setting these pieces spinning as well as revolving about the central Sun. At first each piece would be all gas, like the surface of the Sun it came from, but speedily it would cool, and condense into a liquid globe, and soon, cooling further, would shrink to its present size and solidity. One of these globes would be the Earth, another its attendant Moon.

We now know that Buffon was quite wrong about his "comet." No comet we have ever observed has a mass more than perhaps a millionth part of that of the Earth. On the other hand, the great planets Jupiter and Saturn have masses 317 and 95 times that of the Earth, and two, Uranus and Neptune, not even known in his day, have masses 15 and 17 times that of the Earth. So no real comet is anywhere nearly heavy enough to do the gigantic trick. Why then, if Buffon's facts were so wrong, can we call his theory of comet collision "scientific"? Simply because he sought to explain the unknown by the known, the mystery of the origin of planets by the comets which actually do exist. Too little was then known of the comets, so his facts were wrong and his explanation invalid, but he was using the method of science, which in the end will give true answers if we manage to get and keep our facts straight.

## The Nebular Hypothesis

About the same time, a rival theory was broached independently by Thomas Wright of England and by the scientist-mystic Emanuel Swedenborg of Sweden, both probably inspired by the then recent telescopic discoveries of the dimly seen spiral clouds which we call galaxies. This theory was soon adopted by the German philosopher Immanuel Kant, who in 1755 published it as an essay on the nature and history of the heavens. He assumed that in the beginning a great cloud of gas spread out into space, extending beyond the orbit of Saturn, then the outermost known planet, at a distance of nearly nine hundred million miles from the Sun. This nebula would be slowly drawn inward toward its gravitational center. Kant then assumed that thereby a circular motion would be automatically started (a mistake), and as the cloud contracted, that the speed of rotation would be increased. Most of the gas cloud would condense as the central Sun, which would take on the rotation of the whirling cloud. But here and there parts of the cloud would pack into smaller globes to make the several planets, our Earth among them, all traveling around the Sun and rotating on their own axes in the direction of original cloud rotation.

This idea, however, apparently gained no real following, for when, in 1796, the celebrated mathematician, Marquis Pierre Simon de Laplace, published a somewhat similar theory, he seemed to know nothing of Kant's idea. However, he did know about Buffon's collision theory and criticized it by contending that matter thus knocked off the Sun would have to revolve thereafter in greatly elongated orbits instead of the nearly circular paths actually followed by the planets. This objection, we have since learned, was not well taken.

Laplace had already published a great work, *Celestial Mechanics*, on the movements of the heavenly bodies, and had thereby earned his reputation as the "Newton of France." He followed this with a book on the System of the World in which he presented his new theory, the Nebular Hypothesis.

Being the foremost authority of his day on celestial mechanics, he did not make the gross mistake of Kant of providing an impossible origin for the planetary motions of revolution and rotation. He merely assumed that the Sun was already rotating, without saying why. To explain the vast cloud of gas, he further assumed that the Sun exploded and ejected part of its atmosphere out beyond the orbits of the planets. But by this time, Sir William Herschel had more than doubled the required diameter of the nebula by discovering the planet Uranus circling nearly 1900 million miles from the Sun. The explosion, Laplace explained, "may have occurred from causes like those which gave rise to the brilliant flaring up for months in 1572 of the famous star in Cassiopeia." The violence of this supernova explosion, we now know, was certainly more than adequate for producing such a vast nebula.

According to Laplace, the original rotation of the Sun was transmitted to the nebula at the time of the explosion. And because it was rotating, the gas cloud took on a flattened disc shape, quite like the familiar shapes of many spiral galaxies, though on a much smaller scale, as we have since discovered. Gravitation, of course, was pulling the cloud inward toward the Sun, while the rotation tended to drive it outward. At first the rotation was slow, and gravitation dominated so the cloud shrank slowly to smaller size. But as it became smaller, its rotational speed increased, for the same reason that a skater, turning slowly with his arms extended, suddenly starts spinning dizzily when he draws his arms down close to his body. The reason is the constancy of *angular momentum*, which requires fast motion near the center of rotation to keep it equal to slow motion farther out.

At any rate, Laplace's lens-shaped cloud spun faster as it shrank, increasing the tendency to tear apart. He assumed that as a result an outer ring of gas would separate from the central cloud, and this ring would then gather at some denser point to form a globe of gas, also rotating, and then progressively condense into a solid ball or planet. By having his rotating nebular cloud shed one ring after another, he thus accounted for the formation of all the planets one by one, starting with the outermost. And somewhere in the process of shrinking, spinning, and shedding rings, the satellites of the planets were born by a like process.

### Weakness of the Nebular Hypothesis

It must be said in fairness to Laplace that he was a bit dubious about his own theory, and used words of warning in presenting it. In fact it did have a fatal weakness. That weakness is that the angular momentum of the Sun and planets is distributed unequally. The mass of the Solar System is overwhelmingly concentrated in the Sun, with only 1/700 in all the planets together. But the planets have 98 per cent of the total angular momentum of the System, the Sun only 2 per cent. Roughly, each average unit of planetary mass has 35,000 times more angular momentum than a similar unit in the Sun. And there is simply no way in which this could have been brought about if the Solar System was begun as Laplace suggested.

In due time, other weaknesses of the Nebular Hypothesis were discovered. Thus in 1859, James Clerk Maxwell, the brilliant Scottish physicist, demonstrated mathematically that

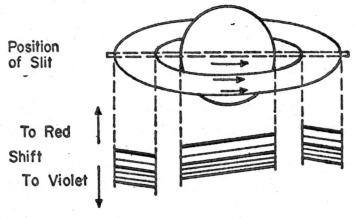

**Position of Slit**

**To Red**

**Shift**

**To Violet**

*Figure 7. Structure of Saturn's Rings*

Keeler's spectroscopic proof that rings are composed of small bodies orbiting about the planet. Spectrum shifts show that the outer edges of the rings are revolving slower than the inside edges. (By permission from *Elements of Astronomy*, Fifth Ed., by E. A. Fath. Copyright 1955. McGraw-Hill Book Co., Inc.)

with swift rotation, Laplace's gaseous rings would not condense into planet globes at all, but would instead stream off into space like mud spattering off a swiftly turning bicycle wheel. Or with slower turning, they might settle down into swarms of smaller bodies circling the Sun in scattered rings.

In this connection, one of the grounds adduced by Laplace for the Nebular Hypothesis was the flat ring system of the planet Saturn, assuming it to be just such a gaseous ring as his theory required. But contrary to theory, it had not condensed into a satellite, a fact later to be found inevitable. In

1715 Jacques Cassini had guessed that Saturn's rings were composed of meteors, and Laplace did realize that the rings could not rotate as a unit. Then in 1857 Maxwell finally demonstrated by mathematics that the rings must consist of myriads of small bodies revolving independently about the planet mass. This was confirmed in 1895 by James E. Keeler when he pointed his spectroscope at the rings to measure the relative speeds of the inner and outer edges as they traveled toward and from us. If the rings revolved as a unit, the outer edge would travel faster. If the rings were a myriad small bodies following separate orbits about the planet, the inner ring edges would travel faster. He found the latter true, and so proved that the rings were a swarm of minute bodies, each moving in its own orbit. But meanwhile, in 1850, Eduoard Roche had shown that a satellite within a distance of 2.44 times the radius of a planet must be broken up by tidal forces. Saturn's rings fall within this limit and are therefore either the fragments of a satellite which moved in too close, or the raw materials of a potential satellite prevented from gathering into a single globe. Incidentally, the American astronomer, Gerard P. Kuiper, has recently announced his conclusion that the ring fragments are chunks of ordinary ice. Be that as it may, the ring system of Saturn is no longer a good argument for the Nebular Hypothesis, but injects facts which cast doubt on its validity.

### The Planetesimal Theory

Eventually the conviction grew that some outside force was required to give birth to the planets and particularly to impart to them their excessive angular momentums. First came the Encounter Theory of Alexander W. Bickerton of New Zealand, published in 1878, which explained everything by a grazing impact between the Sun and a passing star. But it appeared in an obscure biology journal and was therefore missed for half a century by the astronomers. Meanwhile in 1900 the geologist Thomas C. Chamberlin and the mathematical astronomer Forest Ray Moulton, both of Chicago University, had put their heads together, carefully studied the possibilities, and developed the "Planetesimal Theory." They too began with a rotating nebula (produced by the tidal action of a passing star). But they assumed that this nebula was composed largely of small solid particles instead of just gas. These particles they called "planetesimals" or little planets, the central idea being that such particles would not behave like a gas which always tends to expand and disperse into space, preventing gravitational condensing into planets. Instead the planetesimals would revolve in orbits about the Sun and could presumably bunch up here and there into denser parts of the originally irregular swarm. Once such a bunching-up was started, each bunch would grow by pulling in more planetesimals. And as it grew its gravitational power would also grow, so that it would grow even faster. In other words, each bunch would act as a broom sweeping up the rubbish that got in its way or nearby, and this would go on until its portion of space would be fairly well cleaned out. In fact, the resulting planets even today are growing that way, though probably very slowly, the supply of rubbish being pretty nearly exhausted. Thus we know that our Earth is sweeping up meteors continually, for we see them flashing across the night sky, as friction of high speed through the upper air heats them up to glow and finally to burn to fine ash and gas. And now and then we find meteorites which crashed through to landings because they were too big to burn up completely. Until recently we had no proper idea of the amount of meteoric matter being picked up by the Earth. But now radar enables us to detect meteors by day or night, despite sunlight, moonlight, and clouds, and to estimate their mass closely. The total is surprisingly low, only a few tons per day, which means that planetesimal growth is now insignificant. But past time was very long, and the rate of accretion formerly much greater, so in this the Planetesimal Theory seems to remain plausible.

### Help from a Passing Star

But how did the nebular swarm originate and what gave it the excessive angular momentum now inherited by the several planets? According to Chamberlin and Moulton, the matter forming the swarm was torn loose from the Sun. Buffon's old comet theory was not all wrong; something did tear out a part of the Sun's substance to provide raw materials for the planets. They knew, of course, that no comet could ever have done this. So instead they assumed another Sun (that is, a star) passing near our own Sun. Did star and Sun have to crash head on? Certainly not. Did they just sideswipe? Not necessarily even that. Passing close might be enough. Only the star, they thought, would have to be as big, or even bigger than the Sun. "Perhaps much bigger," says the English physicist M. M. Woolfson, who believes the passing star must have been a hundred times as massive as the Sun, passing within a mere four million miles.

Passing near our Sun, such a star would pull gravitationally on the solar matter, lifting up great surface tides. One tide would lift up toward the passing star, another would lift out from the opposite side. Because the Sun is really a huge globe of superheated gas, its surface seething near the bursting point, such lifting of erupting tides could readily occur. Under other circumstances, most material thus erupting from the Sun's surface would simply fall right back, and nothing important would result. But by following the movement of the passing star, some tidal matter would be pulled far out and given a sidewise swing which would eventually settle down into revolution about the Sun. In short, it would go into orbit. Not much of it would be likely to escape with the passing star because the star would be going by too fast. And as the star passed and fled off and away into space, its ever increasing distance would quickly weaken its disruptive effect on the Sun and its hold on the erupted material. Some of this material, failing to get into orbit, would fall back into the Sun and start it rotating. For rotate the Sun does, though rather oddly. Because it is not a solid body, it does not rotate as a unit, but in about 25 days at the equator, then slower and slower up to about 34 days at the poles. This we know from watching sunspots moving across the solar disc and by measuring surface speeds with the spectroscope.

Undoubtedly the passing star, being just another such seething sun, must have suffered just such disruption by the passing of our Sun. It too would have tidal eruptions, set swinging into revolutions, settling down into planetesimals destined to congregate into its own family of planets, the stepsisters and stepbrothers of our own brood of planets, but all forever fleeing and lost to us somewhere off in the depths of space.

### Difficulties Appear

But reasonable though this theory appears, it also had to be modified, first by the astronomer Sir James H. Jeans, then by the geophysicist Sir Harold Jeffreys. They had doubts over several details and seem to have the better of the highly technical argument. Thus Sir James held that the erupted matter took roughly the shape of a cigar, bulky in the middle to account for the huger planets Jupiter and Saturn, but tapering off toward both ends. Also they thought that the planets, while condensing out of the nebular swarm and gases, were once hot enough to be liquid, rather than always cool and solid. By that they helped to explain why the center of the Earth is much heavier than the outer parts. The heavy materials, while still fluid, could settle to the bottom, in this case to the center.

Also, keeping the planets gaseous or liquid for some time helped explain the origin of their satellites. For at first the newly born planets presumably had long looping orbits coming close to the Sun on each trip around. Later these were to change slowly to nearly circular orbits caused by solar tides and the friction of nebular matter. But in those early days, when the fluid planets passed close by, the Sun lifted great tides within them and even tore out the raw materials from which their moons were to condense. Our own Moon, though perhaps born this way, is suggestively exceptional, as we will learn later.

How long did the cooling down take? According to Sir Harold, only a few thousand years, say about five thousand to condense it from gas to liquid, another ten thousand to form a crust over its surface, cool enough for oceans to accumulate. Where did the oceans come from, and the atmosphere? And when did all this happen? The questions pop out at us, but we must put off these details now because we are still not through with the main problem.

Our scientists are properly very fussy and not so easily satisfied. Thus geophysicist Sir Harold, checking and double-checking his own theory, found difficulties in the distribution of angular momentums and other details. So he later decided that the Sun and star did not just pass, but must have actually collided, at least sideswiped. Was Buffon then right, not of course about his comet, but about the collision of the Sun with a large body from outer space? Probably not, for though the new collision theory did take care of some details better, such as how the planetary matter was erupted from the Sun in suitable form for later condensing, it unfortunately made worse the more basic problem of the angular momentums.

But later the Cambridge professor Raymond A. Lyttleton came to the possible rescue with the idea that the Sun was originally a double star, and the companion was a smaller sun at about the present average distance of the larger planets. It was this companion that the passing star struck, head on so as to smash it into small fragments. Most of these it carried away, but enough debris was left and scattered near the Sun to be retained under its control. Of course this collision readily accounts for both the revolutions and rotations of the planets, and especially for their high angular momentums. However, the theory abounds with special difficulties. The assumed double star presents no real problem, for there are plenty of them, one-fourth or more of the observed stars being double or even multiple. More serious is the necessity that the passing star strike at just the right point and angle and instant to do the job of planet-making, the odds being very heavily against it. Actually, of course, there is no way of figuring just what conditions are necessary, nor what really did happen, in the chaotic cataclysm of such a collision. But if this is the way it did happen, our Earth and its fellow planets came very close to not being born at all. And where would that leave us?

Now that raises another question which lately has become of increasing concern: Are there, out in the Universe, other stars with planet families, among them Earths suitably equipped with land, water, air, and temperatures for the emergence of life, and with enough time behind them for the evolution of that life to at least our degree of intelligence? If planet births depend on the accident of stars passing or colliding, such other worlds with other life must be rare indeed. For we know how widely apart the stars are spaced even in our crowded Milky Way, and how they travel and at what sort of speeds, and from all this we can figure how unlikely close-up passings, and particularly direct hits, must be. The result is an overwhelming doubt that any planet-making encounters ever occur, which makes us feel very lonely in our Universe.

Of course, as no one likes to feel so lonely, there is a very strong temptation to look for and adopt some method of planet-making which does not leave us so utterly alone, some method more likely to have been repeated again and again throughout the Universe. Likelihood of occurrence is in itself a very good argument for any method of planet-making that otherwise fits the facts we know. But we should certainly not accept it just because it assuages our loneliness. That would be just wishful thinking, which is always dubious. On the contrary, we should be even more careful and critical, if an idea satisfies our bias or desire, to check it thoroughly before adopting it as our own.

Lately a couple of theories of planet-making have been offered which do meet at least the requirements of likelihood and repeated occurrence. One is that of dissenter Fred Hoyle who believes that the Sun was originally a double star (quite possible), and that one of the pair exploded as a nova (again quite possible), breaking up into fragments, from planet-size to small particles and gas. As the original twin-star system was already necessarily revolving, the revolutions and rotations of the planets and satellites are readily explained, together with their angular momentums. The explosion itself, however, would not contribute to the angular momentum of the system. And considering the violence of the nova explosions we observe in the heavens, we may well wonder whether much matter would be left near enough to the Sun to condense into a planet family. Particularly we must ask what would happen to the Sun itself that near to such an explosion. But of course, whatever happened, we might reason that the Sun has since had plenty of time to gather itself together again and settle down to the business of being an ordinary star in the billions of years we know must have since elapsed.

### A New Nebular Theory

Still another method of planet-making was more recently thought out by Carl F. von Weizsäcker while he idled as a war prisoner in an English detention camp. It too would give plenty of stars with planets, among them some Earths with life and intelligence. It ties in with the Big Bang as the beginning of our observable Universe. It is based on what we have lately been learning about the differing chemical compositions of the stars and of matter scattered through space on the one hand, and of the Earth (and probably the other planets) on the other hand. It used to be thought that stars and planets were all much alike in chemical composition. The modern view, however, is that the stars and space-matter at least begin with about 99 per cent hydrogen and helium, the two lightest elements, and only about 1 per cent heavier elements. The Earth, on the contrary, is practically all composed of the heavier elements. But how can that be if the Earth was formed from the matter of the Universe? That question was in fact von Weizsäcker's clue to his method of planet-making. Rather oddly, because apparently inadvertently, this answer had already been hinted at in 1935 by Henry Norris Russell of Princeton.

That answer takes us right back to Laplace, but under somewhat different conditions. At first there was a huge lens-shaped nebula of gas and dust already revolving about a condensing solar center, its total mass probably more than a hundred times that of all the planets today. It would be composed of the elements in the proportions found in the stars and space, overwhelmingly hydrogen and helium, and was undoubtedly what remained of the original cloud of matter that condensed to form the Sun itself. Its revolution as a whole, and consequent angular momentum, was adequate for the planets to come, and represented one of the great local swirls in cosmic motion which we trace back to the chaotic violence of the Big Bang.

Proceeding from this start, the hydrogen and helium, being highly expansive gases, would slowly disperse and escape into outer space. That would leave behind the molecules and dust of the heavier elements and compounds which would gradually gather into even larger particles, mixed lumps of matter, and so on up to the planet cores providing strong gravitational centers for attracting and sweeping up more and more of the scattered matter remaining. The odd fact that the planets are made up largely of the heavier elements is thus explained. From their present compositions, Gerard P. Kuiper has recently estimated that, of the original nebular matter surrounding the solar core, only about 1/500 was thus retained in forming the four smaller planets Mercury, Venus, Earth, and Mars, but a larger proportion in forming the giant planets.

### Turbulence Factor

Helping in this congregating of matter was a progressive organizing of its motions. Much of this involves highly technical studies of turbulence eddies and patterns in the general rotational swirl, but broadly put, the original general rotation of the whole nebular mass gradually gave way to separate swirls of matter revolving about the central gravitating Sun in individual orbits, with gradual settling down toward preplanetary concentrations. Secondary swirls within the preplanetary swirls could then result in one or more satellites. Also, as the traffic was relatively crowded, any matter in erratic orbits would in time be drawn into line with the main traffic streams. In the end that would mean nearly circular orbits for the resulting planets.

The big advantage of this theory of turbulent eddies is that it solves better several problems of long standing as to details of the present Solar System. Thus it explains why the original raw material broke up into several planets instead of condensing into just one. The sizes and locations of the swirls, smaller and closer together near the central sun core, larger and wider apart farther out, apparently determined the final sizes and spacing of the planets outward from the Sun. According to von Weizsäcker an inner band of smaller eddies gave rise to the small planets Mercury, Venus, Earth, and Mars, while an outer band of larger eddies resulted in the giant planets Jupiter, Saturn, Uranus, and Neptune. Kuiper, however, modified this by assuming more irregularity in the turbulence eddies.

Between these two groups of planets we now find a swarm of midget asteroids numbering thousands, all revolving in

*Plate* VI. SPIRAL GALAXY IN COMA BERENICES. NGC 4565. Though seen edgewise, the irregularities and edge belt of obscuring dust reveal this thin spindle as a rapidly rotating and therefore greatly flattened spiral. (Mount Wilson and Palomar Observatories.)

*Plate* VII. BARRED SPIRAL IN ERIDANUS. NGC 1300. Typical barred spiral in which the opposite arms start mysteriously from the ends of a cross-bar passing straight through the central core. (Mount Wilson and Palomar Observatories.)

*Plate VIII.* GREAT URSA MAJOR SPIRAL. M 101. NGC 5457. Nearby spiral galaxy, ye outside our Local Cluster. Note heavier, well-knotted arms and smaller core as compare with spirals of Plates I and IV. (Mount Wilson and Palomar Observatories.)

Plate IX. GREAT ORION NEBULA. M 42. NGC 1976. Visible as a hazy patch in the "sword" of Orion, this true nebulosity of starlit dust and gas clouds in obvious turmoil is only about a thousand light years away and therefore within our own Milky Way system. (Mount Wilson and Palomar Observatories.)

*Plate* X. Two Colliding Galaxies in Centaurus. NGC 5128. Probably a thin spira[l] galaxy cutting edgewise through a globular galaxy, the resulting commotion making it th[e] strong radio transmitter "Centaurus A." (Mount Wilson and Palomar Observatories[.]

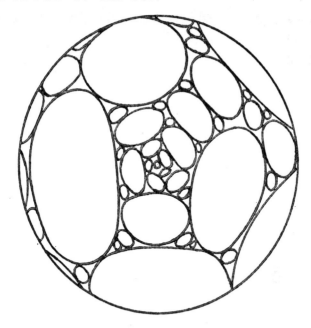

*Figure 8. Turbulence in the Formation of the Solar System*

Weizsäcker's original band of eddies in the solar nebula was quite regular. Kuiper modified it to a more realistic irregular pattern. (After G. P. Kuiper in *The Planets: Their Origin and Development*, by Harold C. Urey, Copyright 1952 by Yale University Press. Reprinted by permission of the publishers.)

individual orbits about the Sun. They may be due to turbulence conditions between the two bands of eddies, or represent a preplanetary swirl which failed to condense, or even a planet formed which then broke up into fragments.

We have understood for some time why a planet in this position should eventually break up or even fail to form. The gigantic mass of Jupiter (more than two-thirds the mass of all the planets) is so dominating that its tidal pull will disrupt any planet formed near it, or more probably, from the very beginning would prevent formation of any such nearby planet.

But we are interested in another result of von Weizsäcker's calculations; how long did the process of planet formation take? His answer is about a hundred thousand years. And how long ago was that? For that figure we must look elsewhere, which we will do in our very last chapter.

### The Likelihood of Planets

In this general connection, Kuiper points out that such formation of planetary systems is closely related to the formation of multiple stars. It is perhaps merely a matter of the relative sizes of the swirls in the presolar nebula, which may depend on such factors as the speeds of rotation, etc. If the component swirls are not too different in size, double or multiple stars may result, each condensation being then large enough to generate its own heat and light as a star. In such cases, any lesser condensation of planetary proportions would likely be absorbed, broken up, or cast off, as any planet orbit relative to two or more large shifting centers of gravitation would certainly be erratic and eventually probably catastrophic in one way or another. But with lesser and merely preplanetary swirls, the single dominating central Sun permits planets to form and survive in individual, regular, and permanent orbits. From which we may conclude that double or multiple stars cannot have planet systems, as they would simply perturb them out of existence.

In the last few pages it is obvious that we have been asking that popular question: Are there likely to be other suns with planets elsewhere in the Universe? We decided that if planets are formed only when stars collide or pass closely, the odds are very much against it. But if (according to von Weizsäcker, and more recently Kuiper and Harold C. Urey—and let us not forget Laplace) planets are born in the normal condensing of a star out of nebular matter, then the Universe should be full, either of double and other multiple stars on the one hand, or of planet families, among them many Earths with right conditions for life to appear and evolve, some few perhaps with beings as intelligent as ourselves (or even as intelligent as we think we are). We see plenty of double and multiple stars, which rather argues for this method of star formation. This also suggests that there are also plenty of planetary systems. But planets, which do not shine by their own light and are only dimly illuminated by reflection, are too small to see at the vast star distances and are quite lost in the glares of their primary suns.

Again we should be warned that our feeling of loneliness and our wishing it so have nothing whatever to do with the actual condensing of planet systems in this manner. Probability is not proof, but merely a fair presumption that this is the way it all happened.

# CHAPTER 6

# EARTH, AIR, AND SEA

As we finally come down to Earth and the matters which concern it more closely, we find ourselves entering a new realm of natural forces and phenomena. This does not mean that, here on Earth, Nature's basic laws somehow change, but merely that we are entering a new range of predominantly lower temperatures in which things do happen differently. Thus far we have been dealing mostly with stars that shine by reason of nuclear reactions which occur because of enormously high temperatures. On the other hand, those temperatures are too high for our familiar chemical compounds to exist and reactions to occur. But now, at the modest temperatures of the Earth and other attendants of the Sun, chemistry begins, with the joining of the atoms of elements into the molecules of compounds, and with their modifications by interchanges of electrons.

In this, the manner of formation and evolution of the planets apparently matters. And conversely, it becomes somewhat possible, by noting the present physical and chemical states of the Earth and other members of the solar family, to infer and then check more or less convincingly on the particular way in which those bodies must have been formed.

This chemical approach has not been entirely overlooked

by past students of the problem of planet origins and development. But they were primarily astronomers rather than chemists. Yet through their spectroscopes, these astronomers have contributed importantly to the field of chemistry, though largely under high-temperature conditions. However, only a few have considered the everyday chemistry of ordinary temperatures in relation to our immediate problem. For example, Henry Norris Russell of Princeton did so at some length in his book of 1935 on *The Solar System and Its Origin*. But finally a great chemist tackled the problem—Harold C. Urey of the University of Chicago, a Nobel Prize winner in chemistry. In 1949 while teaching a summer course on "Chemistry in Nature," he became interested in the problem of planet origins, crammed up on astronomy and did a most creative two-year job of research. In the end, he found himself in general accord with the ideas of von Weizsäcker and of Kuiper, but added significantly to the details of the planet story, first in his Silliman Memorial Lectures at Yale in 1951 and then in a classic book, *The Planets: Their Origin and Development*, in 1952. Though the book is full of mathematics and other technicalities, it has clear, readable summaries which the layman can understand. The presentation which follows covers not only Urey's ideas, but a current consensus to which others have also contributed.

The story of the planets all began with one of those blobs of cold dark gas and dust which show up against the faint background glow of some fairly nearby nebulae. Minute when seen through the telescope, such a blob actually must be huge —according to Kuiper more than ten million times as voluminous as our Sun. Our own particular blob was certainly most diffuse, barely held together by weak gravitational attraction. It was nevertheless contracting very slowly, partly because of gravitation, but perhaps, as Spitzer suggested, even more because of inward pressure by light from surrounding stars. As a minor cosmic swirl, the cloud would be rotating, but with imperceptible slowness. The temperatures were way down near that of space itself, several hundred degrees below our zero. This permitted matter to exist in the solid state, except for hydrogen, helium, and neon, and allowed the formation of chemical compounds, as of iron and other metallic oxides, sulfides, and silicates, water ($H_2O$), ammonia ($NH_3$), methane ($CH_4$), etc.

In earlier chapters we have already traced the development of a star-sun from such an original blob of cold gas and dust. By gradual compacting it becomes an increasingly dense globe, heating slowly both by the compacting itself and by converting gravitational fall into heat energy, until the internal temperature rises to the half million degrees or so which starts the first of the several mass-energy conversions which supply the sun with its long-term and steady heat and light energy. However, at that point we ignored that portion of the original nebular blob which did not fall into the sun, but remained about it as a gas-dust cloud, parts of which were destined to become the family of planets, satellites, asteroids, comets, meteors, etc.

## The Preplanetary Disc

But why did not all the gas and dust of the blob fall into the central sun? There were several reasons. First, the gases themselves were expansive, and became more so as temperatures rose. Also, pressure by the light from the brightening sun would push away dust particles of minute size. And furthermore, the rotation of the cloud would introduce centrifugal forces holding the dust and larger particles, lumps, and planetesimals in balanced orbits at varying distances from the solar center of gravitation. The rotation itself would be due to the initial angular momentum of the original nebular blob. However imperceptible this may have been in its original expanded state, its contraction would increase its speeds and centrifugal effects. By the time its central core became a self-sustaining sun, the surrounding cloud would have become a shapely rotating disc, heated somewhat by the solar radiance, more so near the central sun, less so at increasing distances.

This rotating disc would, however, lack internal stability. To the extent that it was gas, it would tend to expand to a thick disc and to rotate as a unit with higher velocities toward the edges. To the extent that it was separated into orbiting particles and larger units, it would tend to rotate slower toward the edges, swifter toward the center. The result would be that state of near chaos, of collisions, frictions, and drags, best described as turbulence, in which the flow of the whole is broken up into lesser eddies. These, however, are not as haphazard as they seem, but tend to follow patterns. As pointed out by von Weizsäcker and then Kuiper, smaller eddies would form an irregular and shifting band near the Sun, and larger eddies a similar band farther out. From all these eddies there should then form the roughly globular clouds of dust and swarms of lumps which Urey describes as *proto-planets*, smaller ones near the Sun, giant ones farther out.

An important factor in the forming of protoplanet swarms of myriad planetesimal lumps would be the liquid compounds condensed in space from certain gases. Particles of dry dirt or dust do not hang together, but when wet by water they do—as mud. Liquid compounds can therefore serve as coagulants gathering and sticking dust and other small particles together until lumps become large enough to draw and hold other matter by gravitational pull, weak at first, stronger as the units grow in mass. Water and ammonia would be condensed into such effective coagulants out to and including the present orbit of Mars, but beyond that would freeze too dry. In the cooler region from Jupiter outward, methane would similarly serve as coagulant. But between Mars and Jupiter an effective coagulant would be lacking, which may help explain why no large planet formed there.

### Hot Earth Stage

As the globular swarms, in unit sizes from dust to lumps, shrank toward planet solidity, the packing together of the matter would also pack the contained heat and raise the temperatures. Gravitational contraction would also convert to additional heat. At this stage, therefore, the planetary temperatures would rise, up to perhaps 3000 to 4000° F., with a multitude of results.

At such temperatures, gases in general would escape more readily, and even some compounds, such as silicates, might become gaseous and tend to escape. Other compounds would change chemically, such as iron oxides which would lose their oxygen and so concentrate the metal, often as an alloy with nickel. Iron carbide and graphite would become stable, however, and so retain much carbon by preventing its dissipation. Temperatures and other conditions would vary, however, largely with the sizes of the planets and other bodies, and with distance from the Sun. Mercury, for example, seems to have more iron and less silicate rock, while the Moon and Mars apparently have less iron and more rock, as evidenced by their low average densities.

Such interior heating by contraction would be greater in the larger planets, less in the smaller planets, satellites, asteroids, and other bodies. The weaker gravities of the smaller bodies would result in less compacting and heating, and lesser atmosphere retained. So in the smaller planets and lesser bodies there would be less heat to lose, more relative surface to lose it from, less atmosphere to blanket and hold it in, and therefore more rapid cooling of the heat from contraction. The Moon and small planets Mercury and Mars should therefore have solidified sooner, before the iron-nickel could have sunk through to the centers, while in the Earth, and perhaps Venus, these heavy metals could sink down through the still hot and somewhat plastic silicate rocks to form a concentrated central core of great density, a process perhaps still in progress because interior temperatures have remained high enough to permit it.

At the surface of a planet, heat rising from the interior would readily escape into space, leaving the surface at about the temperature determined by solar heating, which depends primarily on nearness to the Sun. Presence of an atmosphere would raise this temperature somewhat by providing a hothouse effect. But Urey thinks that the Earth's atmosphere had been largely lost during the preceding stage of high contraction temperatures, so this blanketing effect would have been absent. Certainly there would have been no such blanketing effect on our Moon and on Mercury, and very little on Mars.

### Renewing the Atmosphere

But if this first solid Earth had thus lost its atmosphere, and its water vapor as well, where did our planet get its present atmosphere, and our oceans of surface waters? Undoubtedly the Earth was then sweeping up planetesimal remains far more rapidly than it does now in the form of meteors, but there would be little air and water added that way. Far more important, probably, were exhalations from the Earth's interior by volcanic eruptions and less spectacularly by slow outward seepage and release through chemical reactions. By such processes, Urey thinks, the Earth at the end of its formation had acquired a new atmosphere of water, hydrogen, ammonia, methane, and some hydrogen sulfide, altogether too full of poisons and too lacking in oxygen for higher forms of life to exist.

But time and chemical change were to cure all that. Thus water vapor in the high atmosphere, acted on particularly by ultraviolet light, was broken up into hydrogen and oxygen. This hydrogen, and that already free, would in due time be lost into space. The oxygen would stay and accumulate. By chemical reactions some of the oxygen would release nitrogen from the ammonia, and carbon from the methane as carbon dioxide, in each case adding to the water supply. Some of the carbon dioxide would react with the silicate rocks to form limestones and sand. And in the course of all this, the chemical conditions probably proved right for life to begin and evolve. And presently, among living things came the green plants which, by consuming carbon dioxide and giving off oxygen, gradually cleared the atmosphere to provide the plentiful supply of oxygen needed for energetic animal life. But how life itself began, and then evolved, will be told elsewhere.

Obviously we have reached that stage of development of earthly conditions under which we live so comfortably. And unless we are indeed thoughtless of the future, we will surely ask if this stage and these conditions are stable and satisfyingly permanent. Particularly we must ask if our central heating plant, the Sun, will go on giving us enough, but not too much, heat and light permanently. We have already learned that it will probably go on quite steadily for several billion years to come, and that will surely do quite well for our human purposes. As to the Earth itself, it seems stable enough in its circling orbit, moving neither too close, nor too far away from the Sun, at least in the near future as counted even in the billions of years. As to its general stability as a solid globe, that too seems permanent enough, at least not subject to another superheating by further gravitational contraction. However, as we will see in the chapters to come, the future stability of the crust, and even its comfortable habitability, remain somewhat open to question.

We may also have to worry a bit about its atmosphere. We are constantly adding to its carbon dioxide content by burning for heat and power, and by increasing the ratio of agricultural to forest areas. We must see to it that adequate plant life is maintained, to clear the air of excess carbon dioxide and to replenish needed oxygen. But as the eons pass, will not that beneficent oxygen escape into space, and perhaps even our water supply, either as water vapor or broken up into hydrogen and oxygen, to leave us perishingly dry? We have already mentioned such escape of atmospheres and water supplies, at least from the Moon and smaller planets, and so had better look into that possibility more closely.

### Retaining an Atmosphere

The free gases making up the atmosphere of any planet or kindred heavenly body are held on entirely by gravitational attraction. And only three factors are important in determining whether they will be held or lost, namely: the surface gravity of the planet, the nature of the gas, and its temperature. We will consider each in turn.

The force of gravity at the surface of any planetary body

is the result of the relation between its mass and its size. The heavier the mass, the greater the gravity pull at a given distance. But the larger the size, the smaller the surface pull just because the surface is farther from the center of pull. The resultant surface gravity should obviously be easy to work out if we know the mass and the body size in the given case. However, for present practical purposes this surface gravity is most usefully stated as the velocity which will enable any bit of matter to get away from the gravitational control. This idea has become quite familiar to us all in connection with space rockets. We know that a rocket must leave the Earth's atmosphere at a speed of seven or more miles per second, or it will not get away. At that speed the planet's gravitation cannot stop it. The Earth's pull will slow up the rocket somewhat, but as the force of gravity weakens rapidly with distance, it can never wholly stop the speeding body, which therefore gets away for good. And what is true for rockets is equally true for any other object, however small, down to the very molecules of a gas. At speeds less than the critical escape velocity, the gravitation of a planet will slow the object (or molecule) down to a stop and then drag it back. In Table A are given the several escape velocities in miles per second for the Sun, the planets, and their large satellites.

We have already learned that gases consist of molecules rushing about at high speeds, bumping into each other, changing directions when bumped, and tending always to expand and therefore escape. In a cubic inch of air (at 32° F. and normal sea-level pressure of one atmosphere) there are about a half-billion billion molecules, traveling at speeds averaging a bit less than a third of a mile per second, but colliding on the average within 1/200,000 of an inch. These collisions transfer energy from one molecule to another, changing their directions and speeds of travel, and generally preventing any mole-

## Table A.  SUN, PLANET, AND SATELLITE DATA

| Sun or Planet Satellite | Earth = 1 Relative Distance from Sun | Relative Radiation Received | Temperature of Visible Surface Calculated | Measured | Earth = 1 Diameter | Mass | Escape Velocity Mi./Sec. | Factor Adjusted for Temperature |
|---|---|---|---|---|---|---|---|---|
| Sun | | | | 11,000° F. | 109.1 | 332,100 | 383. | 82. |
| Mercury | 0.387 | 6.7 | 680° F. | 620° F. | .380 | 0.047 | 2.44 | 1.65 |
| Venus | 0.723 | 1.9 | 150 | 140 | .957 | 0.826 | 6.45 | 5.84 |
| Earth | 1.000 | 1.0 | 60 | 60 | 1.000 | 1.000 | 6.95 | 6.75 |
| Moon | | | 240 | +253 to −214 | .273 | .0123 | 1.47 | 1.22 |
| Mars | 1.524 | 0.43 | −40 | +32 to −40 | .532 | .108 | 3.13 | 3.13 |
| Jupiter | 5.203 | 0.037 | −230 | −220 | 10.95 | 318.4 | 37.5 | 52.8 |
| Io | | | | | .29 | .0134 | 1.5 | 2.1 |
| Europa | | | | | .25 | .008 | 1.2 | 1.8 |
| Ganymede | | | | | .40 | .026 | 1.8 | 2.5 |
| Callisto | | | | | .41 | .007 | 0.9 | 1.3 |
| Saturn | 9.539 | 0.011 | −290 | −240 | 9.15 | 95.2 | 22.4 | 33.7 |
| Titan | | | | | .33 | .023 | 1.8 | 2.7 |
| Uranus | 19.182 | 0.0027 | −340 | −300 | 3.90 | 14.65 | 13.5 | 27.4 |
| Neptune | 30.057 | 0.0011 | −365 | −300 | 3.50 | 17.16 | 15.4 | 34.9 |
| Triton | | | | | .39 | ? | ? | ? |
| Pluto | 39.518 | 0.00064 | −380 | −300 | .46 | .01 | 1.0 | 2.6 |

The first four columns show relative distances from the Sun, the consequent relative radiations received, the resulting calculated temperature of the visible surfaces, and the actual temperatures as measured. The next three columns give the relative diameters and masses and the resulting escape velocity factors for gases, etc. The last column gives escape velocity factors (adjusted for measured temperature of the visible surfaces) for direct comparison with standard gas velocities as given in Table B and those velocities adjusted for complete gas loss in the several periods indicated.

cule from going far enough to get away for good. But at the
outer levels of a planet's atmosphere, the gases become very
thin, the molecules farther apart, the collisions less frequent,
and the chances of getting through and away much greater.

The actual velocities of individual molecules vary in any
mixture of gases such as an atmosphere. In general, the
lighter molecules travel faster, the heavier molecules slower.
All their velocities vary with temperature, moving faster at
higher temperatures, slower at lower temperatures. Table B

### Table B. MOLECULAR VELOCITIES OF GASES

| Gases of Planetary Atmospheres | Molecular Weights | Normal Velocity Mi./Sec. at 32° F. | Velocity of Escape for Loss of Gas in Period: | | |
|---|---|---|---|---|---|
| | | | 50,000 Years | 30 Million Years | 25 Billion Years |
| Hydrogen $H_2$ | 2.016 | 1.15 | 4.6 | 5.2 | 5.8 |
| Helium $He_1$ | 4.003 | 0.82 | 3.3 | 3.7 | 4.1 |
| Methane $CH_4$ | 16.042 | 0.40 | 1.6 | 1.8 | 2.0 |
| Ammonia $NH_3$ | 17.032 | 0.40 | 1.6 | 1.8 | 2.0 |
| Water Vapor $H_2O$ | 18.016 | 0.38 | 1.5 | 1.7 | 1.9 |
| Nitrogen $N_2$ | 28.016 | 0.31 | 1.2 | 1.4 | 1.5 |
| Oxygen $O_2$ | 32.000 | 0.29 | 1.2 | 1.3 | 1.4 |
| Carbon dioxide $CO_2$ | 44.01 | 0.25 | 1.0 | 1.1 | 1.2 |

Includes all important gases of planet atmospheres. Normal velocities of
gas molecules depend on their molecular weights. Loss of a gas from a planet
atmosphere will occur in the period shown if the factor in any of the last
three columns equals the factor shown for the planet or satellite in the
last column of Table A.

shows the normal velocity in miles per second at 32° F. for
each of the gases found in significant amounts in planet
atmospheres. Perhaps you have already found what looks
like a mistake; that water is not a gas at 32° F. You are right,
of course, but the 0.38 miles per second of Table B is still
quite right for a lone molecule of water making a dash for
escape at the outer borders of our atmosphere. We can readily
compute the velocities at any higher or lower temperatures,

but as you will see from Table A, there are so many different planet temperatures to consider that we would need a very big Table B if we tried to accommodate them all. So instead we use a very convenient mathematical trick. Instead of raising or lowering the actual molecule velocities, we simply adjust the escape velocities of the planets and satellites in Table A to equivalents based on their measured temperatures. That also permits us to add three columns to Table B which are most pertinent to our present problem, the permanence of any given planet atmosphere.

Clearly then, the surface temperature of a planet is a very important factor in the retaining of an atmosphere. To begin with, the farther a planet or moon is from the Sun, the less heat and light it receives, and the lower its temperature, at least at the visible surface, which may be on the solid ground in some instances, at the top of the atmosphere in others. More precisely, the radiations from the central Sun spread out in area covered with increased distance, and so must weaken in proportion to the square of the distance. For example, the amount of radiation received at twice a distance is not 1/2, but 1/4; at thrice the distance, not 1/3, but 1/9; etc. So knowing the relative planet distances, we can readily figure the relative amounts of heat and light they receive. From this we can then make good guesses at their probable surface temperatures. A factor at this point is whether the planet is rotating rapidly or slowly, the slow rotation resulting in a higher temperature on the sunlit side, but a much colder one on the dark side. Presence or absence of an atmosphere also makes a difference, the planet with an atmosphere being somewhat warmer. Considering everything, however, we can usually make a fairly good guess at surface temperature. Fortunately, too, we can often measure such temperatures directly by proper (but often tricky) instrumental observations. The calculated guesses and the measured results are roughly in agreement, with any small discrepancies of no practical consequence. Table A, on Planet and Satellite Data, gives what we know of temperature conditions.

But now, before we get down to actual cases, there is another vital item to consider. The normal velocity of a gas molecule is really a sort of average. Some molecules of hydrogen, for example, travel slower, others faster, up to ten, twenty or a few even a hundred times faster than the average. This means, of course, that a few molecules, traveling at higher speeds at the outer levels of a planet atmosphere will escape into space even if the averages of escape velocity and surface gravity would indicate otherwise. Then, given enough time, a planet will thus slowly lose that gas from its atmosphere completely, unless the gas is somehow replaced, or locked up by freezing to a liquid or solid state, or by chemical combination in some solid, liquid, or heavier gas compound. How much time will be needed for complete loss by such leakage will depend on the relative escape velocity of the planet involved, a problem solved by computations made by Sir James H. Jeans. He concluded that if the escape velocity on a planet is as little as 4 times the normal molecule velocity of a given gas, that gas would still be completely lost in about 50,000 years; if 4.5 times, then in 30 million years; and if 5 times, then in 25 billion years. Now this last is for all practical purposes equivalent to eternity. On the other hand, 30 million years is well within the age of the Earth and other planets, during which their atmospheres could have been completely lost.

On this basis, the last three columns of Table B give the escape velocities at which the several gases will be wholly lost in these three critical periods. These velocities should be compared with the adjusted equivalence factors in the last column of Table A. If the escape velocity for total loss of any gas in the 25 billion years column approximates the equivalence factor for a given planet or satellite, that gas should be retained in its atmosphere today. But if that factor is near or below the gas velocity for 30 million years, then the gas is probably missing from that atmosphere.

### The Planet Atmospheres

Such a working comparison between the two tables leads us to expect no atmospheres for our Moon, complete atmospheres for the Earth, Venus, Jupiter, Saturn, Uranus, and Neptune, and thin atmospheres for Mars and perhaps Pluto and the satellites Ganymede (of Jupiter) and Titan (of Saturn). Very rare atmospheres are just possible for Mercury and the Jupiter satellites Io and Europa. Mercury, however, is very close to the Sun, and subject to extremely powerful light pressures, repellent magnetic forces, and other factors which probably upset our best guesses. Otherwise all this is quite in accord with the facts as far as we can observe them.

Among such observed facts are these: All the giant planets have deep atmospheres apparently lacking in our familiar oxygen, carbon dioxide, and water vapor, but with nitrogen, the lighter gases hydrogen and helium, and a strong mixture of methane (the deadly marsh gas), making them all poisonous for living beings. Jupiter and Saturn also show a lot of pungent ammonia gas (frozen out of the colder Neptune and Uranus atmospheres). The lack of water vapor in all the giant planet atmospheres is probably due to its being frozen into shells of ice thousands of miles thick surrounding the heavy planetary cores of iron and rock. Among the smaller bodies, Venus has an atmosphere about as thick and dense as that of

Earth, but filled with opaque clouds so we cannot see the solid surface, and Mars has a very thin atmosphere in no way comparable to that of Earth. Our Moon has no atmosphere that we can detect, though a recent report suggests a shallow emanation of hydrogen and argon gases released by the action of light, but dissipating quickly into space. Some further pertinent details on the planet atmospheres will be taken up in the chapter on Life on the Planets.

### The Earth's Atmosphere

As to the atmosphere of the Earth, we do know a great deal about that, even though its upper reaches have to be explored by indirect means and by theory, and still present mysteries. Thus we know it has a mass of about five million billion tons, which seems immense until we realize it is less than a millionth of the mass of the Earth itself. It is denser at the bottom, gradually thinning out upward until it merges into the relative emptiness of space. This is because the pressure at each level must be just enough to support the weight of all the air above it. Half of its total mass is therefore within 3 1/2 miles of the surface of the Earth, three-quarters within 7 miles, and 99 per cent below 20 miles. Yet it is known, from the height of auroral displays (northern lights), that some atmosphere must still exist up to at least 700 miles, so that its total thickness is roughly a sixth of the radius of the solid Earth. Even at 75 miles up it remains dense enough for infalling meteors to become brightly visible, as friction and air resistance heat them up to the melting and vaporizing points. Yet of this great thickness, only the bottom hundredth is dense enough to support life in health and air-conditioned comfort.

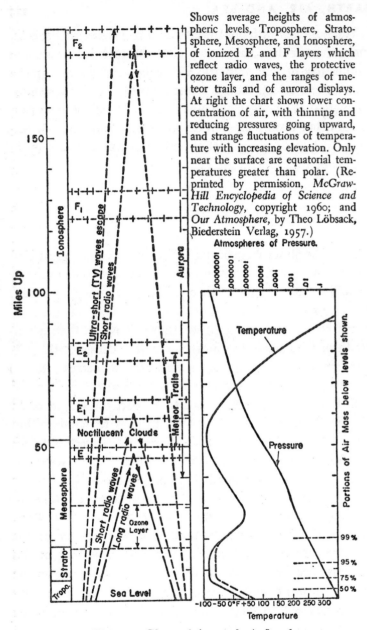

Shows average heights of atmospheric levels, Troposphere, Stratosphere, Mesosphere, and Ionosphere, of ionized E and F layers which reflect radio waves, the protective ozone layer, and the ranges of meteor trails and of auroral displays. At right the chart shows lower concentration of air, with thinning and reducing pressures going upward, and strange fluctuations of temperature with increasing elevation. Only near the surface are equatorial temperatures greater than polar. (Reprinted by permission, *McGraw-Hill Encyclopedia of Science and Technology*, copyright 1960; and *Our Atmosphere*, by Theo Löbsack, Biederstein Verlag, 1957.)

Figure 9. *Chart of Atmospheric Levels*

With increasing height and thinning of the atmosphere, changes in temperature occur. For the first few miles the temperature drops sharply down to about —60° F. through the layer of storms and clouds which we call the *Troposphere*. The next few miles upward comprise the *Stratosphere*, through which the temperature remains fairly constant, except for a slow rising near the equator. Above this is the *Mesosphere*, in which the temperature first rises sharply to about 32° F. at the thirty-mile level, then falls off again to nearly a hundred below zero at the fifty-mile level. Above that is the *Thermosphere* in which temperatures rise sharply up to several thousand degrees. That is due to the direct unshielded rays of the Sun, which speed up the air molecules to high-temperature velocities. Were we up there, however, we would not feel this air heat because of its scattered thinness. But we would be burned up by the direct rays of the Sun, unless we could get into some shade where we would probably freeze to death.

Fortunately, the substantial amount of atmosphere above us serves in several ways as a most effective shield. First, its resistance and friction heat up the swift meteors falling in from space so that nearly all of them burn up into fine ash instead of raining down on us as a deadly hail of solid bullets. Second, it intercepts the high-velocity and potentially dangerous cosmic rays, converting them step by step to lower velocities and lesser danger as they descend to our surface level. And third, it filters out and tempers the rays of the Sun to a comfortable intensity, frequency, and warmth. Much of this shielding against sunlight occurs in the upper atmosphere where the ultraviolet portion is largely absorbed. When thus absorbed, the ultraviolet performs work, decomposing water vapor and ionizing free oxygen to form ozone, composed of molecules of oxygen with three instead of the normal two atoms. Such chemical changes liberate heat and account for the sharp rise in temperature in the lower Mesosphere. Such absorption of the overly intense sunlight is of course a real lifesaver because it cuts off the major portion of the ultra-violet which is so destructive to all living things. Considering the total shielding effect as we know it now, we realize that Shakespeare spoke with unknowing and prophetic wisdom through Hamlet in the words, "This most excellent canopy, the air."

It is fortunate too that the ozone is largely confined to the upper atmosphere. For contrary to everyday opinion, ozone in any appreciable quantity is deadly poison.

Another aspect of the atmosphere shielding is more of a mixed blessing. High in the atmosphere the ionizing energy of sunlight produces several layers of electrically charged air, their region being therefore called the *Ionosphere*. As these layers reflect radio waves of ordinary length, we do take advantage of them to bounce radio beams to distant points over the horizon, but they also hamper us in receiving and sending such waves from and to outer space. However, if we use longer radio waves, those between several inches and several feet in length, the waves do get through the Ionosphere layers and now permit us to penetrate deeply into many secrets of the outer Universe. Fortunately such long waves penetrate obstructions such as clouds of dust in outer space which effectively block the light rays we use in seeing. So now we have two windows to the outer Universe: the old, but rather narrow band of ordinary light and infrared rays; and now a wider band of long radio waves which we use in that promising new science, radio astronomy. Nature has given us a pair of eyes, organs for seeing through the narrower window. But unfortunately, Nature has had no occasion for developing such organs for scanning the revelations available through the wider window. For that we must invent and construct those instruments we call *radio telescopes*, which are not properly telescopes at all, since they form no two-dimensional images. They are actually super-antennae for detecting extremely weak radio disturbances, which we must then somehow translate into meaningful images.

So in considering the physical evolution of our planet, we must regard the evolution of its atmosphere as highly important. Today it serves us as a shield against deadly meteors, cosmic rays, and ultraviolet light. It serves by its greenhouse effect, admitting light and heat rays but retarding their escape back into space, and thereby warms somewhat our surface world of life, tempering the extremes of zonal heat and cold, and fairly equalizing between day and night. It provides a plentiful supply of energy-releasing oxygen by which we are able to lead our active lives more intensely. And by its shifting winds, it does something important which we have not yet mentioned. It carries moisture over the land, there drops it, and so starts the cycle of erosion and deposition, the long process of constant surface change which we recount as Geologic History.

### The Earth's Oceans

The oceans resulted when the water vapor of the early atmosphere finally rained down upon a crust sufficiently cool to retain them as liquid water. Today those oceans cover 70 per cent of the Earth's surface and contain 97 per cent of its free surface water. They too serve vitally in making our Earth habitable by living beings. They provide the reservoir of moisture which the winds carry to water the land and sustain its life. They also provide reservoirs of warmth and coolness which those winds carry landward to moderate climates and diversify our weather.

The winds themselves are ever moving, driven by differential heating by the Sun, and guided largely by the rotation of the Earth. Some move with constancy in zonal belts, and these particularly set up major currents on the ocean surface. To these are added currents even to great depths, set up and controlled by Earth rotation, differential heating, variations in saltness and density, etc. And dominating all are great ocean tides sweeping ever westward, pulled by the gravitations of Moon and Sun, and waxing and waning as those bodies pull together or in opposition. Those tides are to prove a major force in determining the course of development of both Moon and Earth, and even of the life evolving upon the Earth. So the next chapter particularly will tell the story of the shaping of Moon and Earth, how they mutually changed each other, and as a result gave us the World upon which we live.

# CHAPTER 7

# THE CAREER OF THE MOON

ACCORDING to the *Proverbs* of John Heywood, dated 1546, "The Moon is made of a greene cheese."

While we need not take this too seriously, it does raise the question of the composition of the Moon. And that, we are now beginning to realize, probably depends largely on the manner of its birth and growth. We will find that many other Moon questions are also tied up with the story of its origin and career. Furthermore, as we will soon discover, the Moon was a major factor in shaping the course of at least surface events on the Earth itself, and so belongs very much in our story.

Some of the other planets also have moons, but the Earth's Moon seems really different. Some are actually larger in miles and mass, but none is anywhere nearly as large in comparison with its primary. For our Moon is 2160 miles in diameter, over 1/4 the Earth's diameter, its volume about 1/50 and its mass 1/81. No other satellite, compared with its primary, is more than a thousandth in volume. And for satellites of known masses, the largest is less than 1/4000 of its primary. So our Moon is distinctly in a class by itself, wielding more influence on its planet, and perhaps even originating in a different way.

### Lengthening of Day and Month

Some astronomers and geophysicists think that the Moon was born of the Earth. This theory was first proposed in 1878 by the astronomer Sir George H. Darwin (son of the evolutionist Charles Darwin), but described by himself as possibly "wild speculation", and since modified in mathematical details by others. In a sense the story is told backwards, starting with things as they are today, with the present 24-hour day of the Earth's rotation, the present 27 1/3 days of the Moon's month of revolution about the Earth, the Moon's present average distance of 238,860 miles from the Earth, and the present powers of its tidal pull, and that of the Sun, on the oceans of the Earth. Very important is the friction of ocean tides as they flow over the sea bottoms, especially the shallow seas, for they act as great brake shoes to slow up the rotation of the Earth. In fact, that braking action means that if we go back a billion years or so, the Earth must have been spinning at a great rate, once in only a few hours. What would have happened then?

We know very well the effect that the Earth's 24-hour rotation now has on its shape, making it bulge at the equator, flatten at the poles. Its diameter through the poles is 7900 miles, but through the equator 7927 miles, a difference of about 1/300 of its diameter. But the planet Jupiter, rotating every ten hours, has an equatorial bulge of 1/16, while Saturn, with a like rotation, has one of 1/9 its diameter. Evidently the faster a planet rotates, the more it bulges. The reason is well understood. Each particle of matter near the equator is simply trying to fly off into space along the straight line it is traveling at each given instant. We call the resulting tendency *centrifugal force*, which means simply *flying from the center*. We see it in action when a bicycle wheel spatters mud, and you can feel it yourself by swinging any heavy object round and round. The same force also causes grindstones to burst when they are revolved too fast. However, the spinning planets neither burst nor spatter because gravitation is too strong and holds them together.

### Moon Born of Earth

Yet if we think back to the high-speed rotation days of the early Earth, do we not come to a time when it rotated so rapidly that it must have flattened to a watch shape and burst like a high-speed grindstone? If it had, we and our Earth would not be here now. Sir George Darwin himself thought that many fragments did break off, but were held by the Earth's gravitation in nearby orbits, finally reassembling to form the Moon. Some, however, think the Earth would instead have gone through several queer shapes: first bulging at the equator like an orange, then drawing out into a cucumber shape, then becoming pear-shaped (one end larger, the other smaller), and finally, the small end pulling off, leaving the large Earth and the small Moon revolving closely about each other. Thus, some think, the Moon was born.

Of course, there is more to the story than that. Thus when the Earth was itself first born, it was probably larger than now, less dense, presumably hotter, and at least partially fluid. Also it was rotating at some speed slower than the critical bursting speed we have just considered. But it was cooling, shrinking as it cooled, and this would speed up its rotation, eventually to near the bursting speed.

Important too, there was help at hand at the Moon-birth. The Sun had a part in it. For the pull of the Moon was raising tides in the old Earth, tides which circled it with each rotation, tides that went deeper than any surface ocean, into the very substance of the hot plastic Earth itself. That tidal pull helped the Moon break away from the Earth. But how could that be? We know that the Sun's tidal pull is not very strong, only about half that of the Moon today, and capable of lifting the ocean waters only a foot or so upward. How could such a slight pull give sufficient help to bring about this enormous cataclysmic disruption of the old Earth?

Consider, however, what a small force can do if you let it pile up. You can give a playground swing a series of slight pushes, each one adding a bit to the rhythmic motion, until it swings very high indeed. You must of course give each push at just the right instant, in time with the swing itself. If you push at the wrong time, you get knocked over, and the swing is stopped. The swing has its own to and fro period, and a small force applied repeatedly in time with that period can produce a big effect. That is how the heavy pendulum of an old-style clock is kept swinging—by the piling up of repeated slight pushes applied through the escapement mechanism.

So it would be with the ancient Earth. It had a natural period of elastic oscillation of a very few hours. When its rotation was speeded up to that same period, each circling solar tide tended to pile up on those before it. Because these were tides of the fluid body of the Earth itself, their piling up was enough to precipitate the final disruption of the mass nearly ready to be pulled apart by its rapid rotation. The piling up would have to be considerable, but once the rotation period got in step with the natural period of oscillation, it has been estimated that only about five hundred years would be needed to bring about the Moon's separation, and that, for a cosmic event of such magnitude, was a very short time indeed.

And still another factor may have played a part in precipitating the Moon's break off from the Earth. At that time the Earth's orbit about the Sun may have been much more eccentric, so that once each year the Earth-Moon mass would have come much closer to the Sun, thus greatly increasing the disruptive tidal pull. It is a fact that the eccentricity of the Earth's orbit does change, but that change is cyclic over a varying period of from 60,000 to 120,000 years, with a mere waxing and waning in the eccentricity. But it has also been surmised that when the Solar System first took form, the planetary orbits were all more eccentric, gradually becoming more nearly circular. In either case, this factor may have played a somewhat uncertain part at the Moon-birth.

Some scientists think that this is what did happen. The Moon was thus born and at first stuck close to the Earth. They revolved about each other and also rotated in practically the same period. Because of nearness, their mutual gravitational pulls must have been enormous, lifting great protuberances toward each other so that they looked like two eggs swinging round and round, their small ends pointing inward. Of course, one was a huge ostrich egg for size, the other just a hen's egg. Then gradually they drew apart, the Moon in an ever widening orbit, thereby making its month longer. Also the rotations of both Earth and Moon slowed up, that of the Moon more so, until now it rotates only once per revolution, thereby always keeping the same face toward the Earth. Meanwhile the Earth's rotation was also retarded, until now its day is twenty-four hours long.

### Tides and Moon Recession

While the braking action of the tides on the Earth's rotation is readily understood, what really seems mysterious is that those same tides should drive the Moon slowly farther from the Earth and slow up its period of revolution so as to make the month longer. Yet the scientists tell us that this is so. Without going into the mathematical details, this is what happens. The Earth rotates and the Moon revolves in the same direction, from west to east, the Earth many times faster. The rotating Earth, by friction, drags the tidal bulge always somewhat eastward and therefore ahead of the Moon. Being thus ahead, the tidal bulge also pulls slightly forward on the Moon mass, and thus slowly increases its speed of travel. But such higher speed in the orbit increases the centrifugal force, which draws the Moon a little farther away into a somewhat larger orbit so that its revolution takes longer for the round trip and even slows up its speed. This sounds contradictory, but technically what happens is that angular momentum is deducted from the Earth's rotation and added to the Moon's revolution.

Good estimates of the present rate of recession of the Moon from the Earth vary from two to four inches per year. Dividing the Moon's present distance of 238,860 miles by these rates, we get roughly from five to ten billion years since the Moon broke away from the Earth. However, when the Moon was much nearer, the recession rate was necessarily much greater, so we should cut down this time considerably. Therefore our date for the Moon's birth should perhaps be only two billion years ago. Unfortunately there are other uncertainties, such as the depths and extents of the oceans in the geologic past which would affect the amount of tidal friction at work, so that we will later have to turn to other more reliable methods for fixing past dates to get at that of the Moon-birth.

This process of Moon recession, we are told, will go on for some tens of billions of years more. Eventually the Moon should be another hundred thousand miles farther away and the month should be about forty-seven of our present days. But the Earth's rotation should then also be slowed up to forty-seven of our present days. As a result, the Moon will seem to hang motionless in the sky, visible only on one side of the Earth, the inhabitants of the other side never seeing it at all.

The lunar tides will then cease to be, but the solar tides will still be acting to slow down the Earth's rotation even more. The slight tidal pull on the Moon will then be reversed and its travel speed reduced. Also it will spiral very slowly toward the Earth until eventually it gets too close. Then the Earth pull will tear the Moon apart to form a ring of fragments just like the rings of Saturn. If humanity then still lives on Earth, every night it may enjoy not mere waxing and waning moonlight, but the bright light from the sunlit portions of the wide ring which extend beyond the shadow cast by the body of the Earth. But very likely there will be no living beings to see all this, for long before such crumbling of the Moon, its nearness and swift flight must raise huge tides rushing over the Earth to sweep away all living things. Besides, it is very doubtful that the Sun itself will still be radiating the right amounts of light and heat needed for maintaining earthly life in this remote future.

But is not all this mostly theory? Have we really any evidence whatever tending to corroborate this startling story, either past or future? The answer, believe it or not, is "Yes."

### Evidence from Ancient Eclipses

First of all it seems to be actual fact that the rotation of the Earth is very gradually slowing down. We all know that our mathematical astronomers can predict eclipses of the Sun and Moon very precisely and for centuries ahead. Also they can "predict" backwards and tell precisely when eclipses of the past should have occurred. But over two centuries ago, the English astronomer Edmund Halley discovered that ancient eclipse records did not agree with the times thus determined. He thought this was due to a speeding up of the Moon's motion, but today these discrepancies are better explained by assuming a slow retarding of the Earth's rotation and a consequent lengthening of the day.

We now know that the Babylonian, Egyptian, Chinese, and Greek astrologers, priests, and even astronomers of two thousand to four thousand years ago kept eclipse records which are very inexact by modern standards. They had neither the need for precision, nor the instruments and skills required. But quite inadvertently they did give us one series of pertinent facts—the places from which they observed the eclipses, and what gave the whole thing away was the fact that they apparently saw them from the wrong places.

A significant peculiarity of a solar eclipse is that it can be seen only along the narrow path followed by the Moon's shadow as it sweeps over the surface of the rotating Earth. Any change of the time of the eclipse will therefore shift its path to the east or the west. And even lunar eclipses, though visible more widely, can only be seen with the Moon above the horizon, again a matter of timing. What concerns us here is that those who recorded the ancient eclipses should not have been able to see them at all, being either outside the computed solar eclipse paths or out of sight of the eclipsed Moon. They were always seeing them from places too far to the west, which indicates that the Earth's rotation has been slowing up.

Furthermore, the amounts of the time discrepancies thus indicated gave us a good idea of the rate at which the rotation is being slowed down. It turns out to be roughly one second per daily rotation in 100,000 to 120,000 years. In other words, that long ago, the day was not 24 hours, but one second less, and that long in the future, the day will be 24 hours plus one second. Of course that means that, say 3000 years ago, the day should have been 3000/100,000 (or 1/33) second shorter than now. But to figure the total difference that would make in the 3000 years, we have to average between the day then and the day now, which gives us 1/66 second per day to work with. We simply multiply this by the number of days in 3000 years to get the total time correction we must apply to our eclipse back-casts, and that amounts to about 4 1/2 hours. By shifting the computed solar eclipse paths and Moon paths westward accordingly, we can explain why the ancient observers were able to see the eclipses they saw and recorded. It is largely on this that we base our belief that the Earth's day is slowly lengthening.

But can we confirm this by accurate modern observations, say over a single century? That would mean a lengthening of the day by only 100/100,000 (or 1/1000) second, and a cumulation of differences over only 100 years. Again we must average the differences over our total period, giving us only 1/2000 second to work with. Multiplying this by the number of days in a hundred years (36,526), we get a total difference of only 18 and a fraction seconds, a rather small amount to check on over a whole century. Yet modern astronomical observations have been accurate enough for a century for us to confirm even such minute differences in timing.

But this really strains all our means for keeping accurate time and must be arrived at indirectly. Our ordinary clocks are not nearly precise enough, and quite obviously we cannot check the Earth's rotation by astronomical time, itself based on that self-same rotation. However, since 1948, the United States Bureau of Standards and other physical laboratories have developed extremely-high-precision timekeepers based on natural oscillations in molecules and atoms. Thus in the ammonia molecule ($NH_3$), the single nitrogen atom flips back and forth through the triangle of hydrogen atoms 23,870 million times per second. Hitched up properly this gives a timekeeping control accurate to about 1/4000 second per day. And we can even improve on this several times by using caesium or rubidium atoms and other ingenious means. In fact, the United States Naval Observatory has just put in a caesium atomic clock as its master time control, with an accuracy of one part in ten billion. With such precision we may soon check directly on the slowing of the Earth's rotation.

### Possible Neutralizing Factor

However, we should not ignore a recent theory by E. E. R. Holmberg, who thinks that rotation is no longer slowing down, though it has done so in ages past. There is now a force neutralizing the braking action of the Moon tides, the tidal pulsation of the Earth's atmosphere. According to Holmberg, the natural oscillation period of the atmosphere, controlled by the composition, density, and temperature of the air, is out of step with the lunar tides and tends to dampen them, thus neutralizing their retarding effect. However, we do not know too well what that natural oscillation period really is. It may vary a bit, say because of a general drop of world temperatures during an Ice Age. So we do not actually know whether our day of twenty-four hours was reached and held some time in the past (the evidence of eclipse records being against this), or perhaps will lengthen for some time to come and then stabilize at some longer period of rotation. In any case, if the day is ever held fixed by the Holmberg effect, two theoretical results are expected: (1) the Moon will still be spiraling slowly outward from the Earth; and (2) the Earth itself will be slowly spiraling inward toward the Sun.

### Absence of Pacific Granites

But another item has been cited as tangible evidence to confirm even more directly the theory that the Moon was born of the Earth. It is the fact that nowhere in the basin of the Pacific Ocean do we find any trace of granite rocks. Elsewhere on the continents and under the oceans, granite is quite common, but not in the Pacific area. The explanation given is this.

Whatever way the Earth was originally formed, by condensing from a gaseous globe or by a congregating of planetesimals, one thing must have surely happened, a sorting of materials by density, the heavier components sinking toward the center, the lighter toward the surface. For, as we shall see in the next chapter, that is how the material of the Earth is arranged now. At the center is a very dense core (probably iron, nickel, etc.), then a thick intermediate shell of mixed rocks somewhat less dense, near the surface a thin shell of lighter basalts, and at the surface an even thinner scattering of still lighter granites.

At some stage we must surmise that the Earth was hot and plastic enough for such sorting to go on. Then must have followed cooling, first on the outside, resulting in a solid crust of granites and some underlying basalts. It was about this time that the Moon was presumably born from materials at or near the Earth's surface, taking with it a large portion of

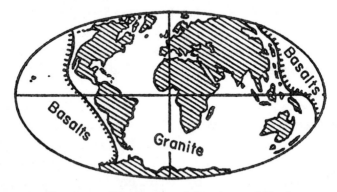

*Figure 10.   Distribution of Granites and Basalts*

Shows lack of granites in Pacific Basin. (From *Biography of the Earth,* by George Gamow, Copyright 1941. Reprinted by permission of the Viking Press, Inc.)

the granite-basalt crust. According to the American astronomer, William H. Pickering, the Pacific Basin is the great scar left on the face of the Earth. Gamow, who is blessed with romantic imagination, suggests that this newborn Moon, at first hanging poised in the sky directly over the Pacific center of its place of birth, should properly be called the "Hawaiian Moon."

### Grect Atlantic Rift

In the travail of such a Moon-birth, events of great violence and lasting effect must have occurred all over the Earth. For example, the very oldest uncovered rocks of the earth-crust, dating back about two billion years ago, are hard to decipher, being apparently former lavas and stratified rocks which have been subjected to cataclysmic violence, with melting heats, terrific pressures, and distorting disturbances. Pickering even believed that what remained of the earlier granitic crust would have cracked into separate continents which would have drifted apart on the substratum of plastic basalt on which they floated. Thus, he surmised, a big irregular north and south crack opened to separate the old and the new world continents from each other, forming the Atlantic Basin between them. To confirm this, he called attention to the opposing coast lines of Africa and South America, which if brought back together, could fit very exactly. Meanwhile, he thought the continental areas around the Pacific scar would slide toward each other by slow drifting.

However, matters were undoubtedly not as simple as this. For one thing, the geologic evidence indicates that the Atlantic rift between the old and new worlds occurred much later than Pickering assumed. So if the broad Pacific be indeed the scar of the Moon-birth, the Atlantic rifting (among others) must have been long delayed. Also it is quite possible that the Pacific Basin is not the Moon-scar at all, even if the Moon was born of the Earth in the manner described by George H. Darwin. For we can reasonably assume that in such a cataclysmic disruption of huge masses, there would be a general melting of any crust that may have previously formed, and subsequently vast Earth-tides and prolonged reshaping of both Earth and Moon from egg forms to oblate globes. During this deep-seated turmoil all traces of any Moon-scar on the Earth would be quite obliterated.

### Objections to Moon Fission

All in all, some very serious doubts have been raised against this whole theory of Earth-Moon fission by tidal pulls and rhythmic build-up. Most serious are the objections of the eminent geophysicist Sir Harold Jeffreys. When he first looked into the theory some thirty years ago, he thought it quite possible. But after more careful study, he decided against it. For one thing, friction would prevent the building up of the necessary tidal protuberance. Second, any such formation of a protuberance would automatically slow up the Earth's rotation and so take it out of step with the natural period of elastic oscillation, effectively stopping the further necessary build-up. These are very difficult obstacles to overcome, and raise most serious doubts as to the birth of the Moon from the body of the Earth.

But what then becomes of the well established astronomical fact that the Earth's day is getting longer, with its related fact that the Moon is receding slowly from the Earth? Is not all that tied up with the Earth-born theory of the Moon and all that this implies? The answer is, "Not necessarily so." Even if there had never been any such fission of Earth and Moon, but instead some other method of separate origins out of condensing knots of gas, dust, and planetesimals in the general process of contraction of a presolar nebula, we would still have left a Moon-Earth pair revolving closely about each other, in which the Moon-pull would produce ocean (and perhaps crustal) tides on the Earth, resulting in a slowing up of the Earth's rotation and increase in the Moon's distance and period of revolution, all going on for some billions of years. This much would then remain the same, including the forecast of the futures of Earth and Moon, only the very beginnings being different. If the evidence so decrees, we can abandon the Moon-birth by fission from the Earth, and still have a consistent story.

That is the position taken by Ralph B. Baldwin of the University of Chicago in his 1949 book *The Face of the Moon,* a true classic on this subject. Basing his calculations upon a present rate of slowing of the Earth's rotation by one second in 120,000 years, and ignoring possible variations in the tidal conditions other than the Moon's increasing distance from the Earth, he offers a table going back two billion years, the approximate age of the oldest rocks we have succeeded in dating. On this table is based the one given below, showing first, how many million years ago, second, the distance of the Moon in miles, third, the corresponding month in our present days (added by us), and last, the length of the Earth's day in hours.

CHANGING RELATIONS OF EARTH, MOON, MONTH, AND DAY

| Millions of Years Ago | Moon Distance (in Miles) | Length of Month (in Days) | Length of Day (in Hours) |
|---|---|---|---|
| Present | 238,860 | 27.3 | 24.0 |
| 620 | 215,000 | 23.3 | 22.8 |
| 930 | 200,000 | 20.9 | 22.0 |
| 1607 | 150,000 | 13.0 | 19.1 |
| 1905 | 100,000 | 7.4 | 15.6 |
| 1965 | 75,000 | 4.8 | 13.5 |
| 1992 | 50,000 | 2.6 | 11.1 |

**Other Moon Origins**

Those who doubt the Earth-Moon fission theory are divided between two theories. One is that Earth and Moon were both born at the same time as a double planet, by separate condensing from two sub-eddies in one general preplanetary swirl, and that the two, being thus originally close together, hung on to each other gravitationally from that day to this.

The alternative non-fission theory is that Earth and Moon were formed quite apart by separate condensing in the course of the general formation of all planets and satellites. But happening to orbit near each other in their revolutions about

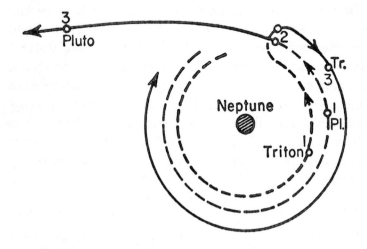

*Figure 11. Pluto as an Escaped Satellite of Neptune*

By permission from *The Modern Universe*, Raymond A. Lyttleton, Harpers, 1957.

the Sun, they captured each other gravitationally and have remained together ever since.

Now most of the satellites, our own Moon among them, revolve about their planets in the same directions as the planets rotate, and close to the planes of those rotations. This rather argues for their birth with the planets themselves, at the same time as their planets were formed and participating in the same local swirls which set the planets rotating. Some few satellites, however, travel in retrograde directions opposite to the rotations of their primaries, or in orbits highly inclined to the planet equators. These would be easier to explain by capture at a later date.

A reversal of such capture is the suggestion by Raymond A. Lyttleton that Pluto, the outermost planet of the solar system, is an escaped satellite of Neptune. Triton, the present satellite of Neptune, revolves about it in a retrograde direction. The theory is that originally both Pluto and Triton revolved about Neptune in the usual direction, with Triton innermost. Tidal drag then caused them both to recede slowly outward from the planet, Triton receding somewhat faster. This brought them closer together in their orbits, until eventually they came too close and swung around each other, with the result that Triton began traveling about Neptune in its present retrograde direction and Pluto, speeding up, escaped into a planetary orbit of its own about the Sun. To this day, Pluto's highly eccentric orbit crosses over inside that of Neptune.

### Shape of the Moon

As you gaze up at the full Moon, you see plainly the shadowy face of the Man in the Moon, a well-mannered gentleman who always faces the company he keeps (Plate XX). For the Moon, as it revolves about the Earth, always turns the same face toward it. So until early October, 1959, when the Soviet Russian rocket Lunik III took a picture and radioed it back to Earth, we could only guess how the far side might look. The near side, however, we have known well ever since that night in 1610 when Galileo first pointed his telescope at it and discovered its rugged surface of craters and mountains and of wide level areas at first mistakenly called *maria* or seas. So plainly visible is that surface that through our visual and photographic observations we have been able to map it with an accuracy far surpassing our maps of the Earth itself, which we can chart only by arduous exploration and careful measurements.

Not so obvious, since it requires tricky and refined measurements, is the discovery that the Moon is slightly egg-shaped, with a small bulge toward the Earth. But though slight, that bulge is still too large to be wholly caused by the gravitational pull of the Earth at the present distance. Rather it is the size that would be produced when the Moon was 70,000 to 90,000 miles from the Earth, roughly one-third its present distance. In other words, it is a fossil tidal bulge from the time (roughly two billion years ago) when the Moon froze to solidity early in its career. That further implies that the Moon's interior was then already sufficiently cool and solid to support the bulge from that time on. From this Urey also concludes that the Moon's interior had a low-temperature origin, and was never hot enough to be plastic and yielding. In effect, this means that it was built up by gradual gathering together of cold planetesimals and not by fission from a spinning Earth. There may have been some surface heating as planetesimals struck, but that would be superficial and temporary, not disturbing the solidity of the Moon as a whole.

### Face of the Moon

The view of the full Moon, even well magnified, shows surprisingly little topographic detail (Plate XX). That is because the Sun is then directly behind us and shining almost exactly straight down on the craters and mountains, which therefore cast no revealing shadows. Of course, shadows are being cast by the irregularities near the edge of the Moon disc, but they are directed away from us and are therefore not visible from our point of view. So about all we see at full moon are the light and dark grays due to differences in color and reflectivity of the various surface areas. Only one group of features stand out more distinctly at this time, the white rays which radiate from certain craters, notably Tycho, Copernicus, and Kepler.

All the other topographic irregularities are better seen during the other phases of the Moon when the sunshine strikes at low angles so as to cast long shadows. Then craters and mountains stand out in bold relief, particularly along the terminator, the edge of the illuminated surface. As the Moon revolves about the Earth, it also rotates relative to the Sun, and the terminator moves gradually eastward (as we see it) to reveal the irregularities at and near its advancing edge. Thus we never see all the craters and mountains at any one time, but of course we can use complementary views as in Plates XVIII and XIX to show nearly all the Moon's features a good deal better. Thus shown, the disc of the Moon reminds us of nothing so much as a face scarred very badly indeed by pockmarks.

The largest of the craters is Clavius, 145 miles across, located near the South Pole (top of map). There are more than thirty thousand moon craters, ranging in size down to actual invisibility to our best telescopes. Many have level interiors, others have central peaks. Some have smaller craters within larger craters, others have marginal walls broken by such small craters. Some stand out boldly from the level *maria*, others seem to be sunken or nearly buried. Because of the sharp curvature of the surface, due to the smallness of the Moon, our own space-travelers, standing on one wall of a wide crater, may not be able to see the opposite wall, it being below the horizon formed by the curvature of the interior plain. In other words,

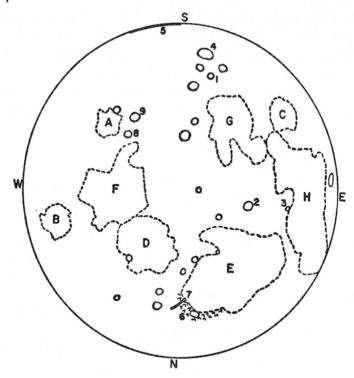

*Figure 12. Key Map of the Moon*

Key to Plates XVIII and XIX, showing the locations of Moon features discussed in the text.

1. Tycho Crater.
2. Copernicus Crater.
3. Kepler Crater.
4. Clavius Crater.
5. Leibnitz Mountains.
6. Alps Mountains.
7. Groove Valley.
8. Theophilus Crater.
9. Catherina Crater.

A. *Mare Nectaris.*
B. *Mare Crisium.*
C. *Mare Humorum.*
D. *Mare Serenitatis.*
E. *Mare Imbrium.*
F. *Mare Tranquilitatis.*
G. *Mare Nubium.*
H. *Oceanus Procellarum.*

the large craters are shallow and could be called dish-shaped except that inside they bulge upward, this despite the fact that walls slope steeply and rise (in the case of Clavius) to 17,000 feet above the interior. These heights, and those of the mountains, are measured by the lengths of the shadows they cast. The very highest are the Leibnitz Range along the south edge of the Moon, rising to about six miles, though this is not very exact because, with no surface waters on the Moon, there is no definite sea level or other base level to refer to. If our own mountains were proportional in size (relative to the Earth), they would rise to twenty miles, well into the stratosphere.

### Are the Craters Volcanic?

Observing these ringed craters, towering mountains and wide-spreading plains, it is most natural to assume that the same geologic forces familiar to us here on Earth must also have been at work upon the Moon. The craters would then be due to volcanic eruptions, the mountains to crustal folding and uplift, the *maria* to great lava flows or perhaps ancient sea beds. However, several facts raise serious doubts and have led to other explanations, often most fantastic, such as the medieval belief that the Moon features were images of those on Earth reflected on a mirror surface. Another absurd theory made these merely odd shapes assumed by a crust of ice, despite the now known fact that the surface temperature rises each month to something like 250° F., well above the melting point of ice. And still another theory made the mountains and craters oddly fixed storms and whirlwinds in an atmosphere, which we now know does not exist, and would not behave that way anyway.

### Craters by Meteor Impact

Compared with such absurdities, volcanic action is a normal and sensible explanation for the craters, were it not for their great sizes and peculiarities of form. Craters up to 145 miles across, but relatively shallow as a dish, are hard to explain as volcanic. Largely to account for these, the meteoric bombardment theory was developed. First offered by the German astronomer P. von Gruithuisen in 1824, soon forgotten, but then revived in 1873 (and presently abandoned) by the English popularizer of astronomy, Richard A. Proctor, it has lately gained wide acceptance, though there are some modern Moon observers of high authority who still refuse to accept it. So again we must consider pros and cons.

One way to check on the meteoric theory was to duplicate it experimentally in miniature, and Alfred Wegener, the German geologist, undertook to do this. First he prepared thin flat layers of powdered cement, using different colors. Into these he threw dabs of soft plaster and noted the results, the colors telling him what substances or layers splashed where. He was thus able to produce typical small-scale lunar craters, and even central peaks and spreading systems of rays, all rather strongly confirming the meteor impact theory.

However, in its modern form, the meteor impact theory is actually an explosion theory, which is not quite the same. For when a meteor strikes the Moon surface at velocities of tens of miles per second, it not only buries itself to a depth several times its own diameter, but also instantly generates tremendous pressures and heat. The result is violent explosion, clearing out a dish-shaped area by scattering the soil, rocks, and meteoric matter outward, and piling up a circular wall to form the typical crater. There will be local crushing of the bedrock underneath, particularly at the impact point where a central peak may then be left. As the final effects are thus due to explosion from a central point, it does not much matter from what direction the meteor arrives; the crater wall will always be quite circular. And crater size will depend largely on the mass of the meteor and its speed of arrival. Thus at thirty miles per second, the explosive energy should be 250 times that of dynamite of equal mass, and at forty miles per second, nearly twice that much, both velocities being quite normal for observed meteors.

Obviously this theory, though developed independently, is quite in accord with the modern versions of the planetesimal theory as worked out by von Weizsäcker, Kuiper, and Urey. Of course this implies much greater meteoric activity in the early days of Earth and Moon formation, with the meteors of larger average size and numbers. Since then we must assume a gradual reduction in both numbers and average size. This helps explain the scattering of small craters within and upon the walls of large Moon craters, and over the wide expanses of the *maria.*

**The Lunar Plains**

The level surfaces of the *maria* are explained by Urey not as extrusive lava flows of volcanic origin, but as flows of rock materials melted by the heat of impact of large planetesimals (say roughly a hundred miles in diameter) arriving at low velocities, presumably from their nearby orbits about the Sun. Arriving slowly, their effects would be less explosive, instead causing only melting and flowage to form the level *maria* surfaces. On the other hand, some of the *maria* are rimmed by mountain ranges which rather suggest super-explosions.

Still another idea, recently broached, makes the smooth *maria* surfaces not lava but beds of fine dust. In the absence of air and water, the dust formation by disintegration of rocks must be due to factors such as expansion and contraction from rapid temperature changes (especially during lunar eclipses), the sand-blasting impacts of fine meteoric particles, and various disruptive solar radiations of light, ultraviolet, X-rays, etc. The flowage (or should we say creepage) of the dust to form the level surfaces can also be explained by a continuous agitation by heat, light pressure, and again those myriads of fine meteoric impacts. It may well be that when our Earthly space-travelers first set foot on the Moon, they had better step out carefully, lest they sink out of sight into such an insubstantial sea of dust.

However, there are good reasons for thinking that the surfaces (except for a few inches of rubble and dust) are solid enough. There are well-marked cracks, cliff escarpments, and large-scale fossil flowage-ripples testifying to surface solidity. On the other hand, careful studies of lags in surface heating and cooling, using sensitive thermocouple thermometers, heat-radio waves, etc., consistently indicate a layer of insulating pumice dust a few inches thick, under which the temperature is uniformly about −40° F. Yet the marked differences in dark and light grays of those surfaces suggest either differences in dust coverage or in chemical composition. Thus Urey thinks the darker areas are iron oxides and sulfides, the lighter areas silicate rocks. Modifying this view of surface and sub-surface, we have the recent report from Thomas Gold, now at Cornell University, that radio waves bounced off the Moon by powerful United States transmitters and picked up by our sensitive radio telescopes, indicate a half-mile thickness of ice starting about a hundred feet below the surface. This frozen layer should retain a considerable supply of water below it in the warmer interior, and because of radioactive heating that interior should become hotter towards the center.

### Order of Final Events

As part of his intensive study of the formation of planets and satellites, Urey pays particular attention to the Moon and tries to trace the final events in the forming of its present features in their approximate order of occurrence. The Moon must have already been frozen into its present slight egg-shape, so that its surface was on the whole rigid. Then at widely spaced intervals as measured by human years, but frequently on the cosmic time scale, meteors, large and small, struck at high velocities, causing violent explosions, and craters of all sizes and aspects, the later ones often damaging the earlier. Now and then some larger mass, virtually a minor planet, perhaps broken up into a swarm of meteors, struck and melted a wide area, with ensuing flowage to a smooth level. On occasion, some huge lump struck a glancing blow, driving surface matter before it, scattering and heaping mountain ranges of both Moon matter and its own meteoric substance. Or if it merely skimmed the surface, it could have plowed just such a long straight groove as we see crossing the lunar Alps for eighty miles near the Moon's North Pole.

We can often readily determine the order of lunar surface events. Thus the Alps must have been piled up before the straight groove valley was cut across them. And the great crater Clavius must have been formed before the several lesser craters which mar its basin and walls. More elusive is the order of formation of the several *maria,* to be judged by less obvious relations. But Urey considers as older the small Mare Nectaris in the southwest quadrant, scarred perhaps a hundred thousand years later by meteor falls forming the explosion craters Theophilus and Catherina. Next in order he puts Mare Crisium in the northwest quadrant and Mare Humorum in the southeast, both of small extent, followed by the larger Mare Serenitatis in the northwest quadrant and the huge Mare Imbrium in the northeast. Imbrium he thinks is due to a large asteroid coming in at a low angle from the northeast at the slow velocity of only 1 1/2 miles per second. Mare Tranquilitatis (west equatorial), Mare Nubium (southeast quadrant), and Oceanus Procellarum (east equatorial), he believes are lava flows resulting from melting by large planetesimals. In the formation of these *maria* it is quite evident that numerous former craters would have been melted down or buried by lava flows, and we often see remnants or outlines of such buried craters, notably in the eastern equatorial area.

Clearly formed after the lava flows had hardened are the scattered and unmarred craters standing out conspicuously on the *maria* and elsewhere. Outstanding among these are several in Mare Imbrium, and those surrounded by systems of strong white rays, particularly Tycho, Copernicus, and Kepler. These rays are now thought to be streaks of dust thrown out by the explosions which formed the central craters. Tycho, placed in the midst of a chaos of earlier craters, appears to be the last important feature added to the Moon's topography. Its rays are the brightest and longest, indicating enormous explosive energy. Some of its rays quite certainly extend to the invisible side of the Moon, while the curvatures of others indicate to Urey a displacement due to a Moon rotation in a period of about twelve hours. This puts even this latest lunar event far back in the slowing up of the Moon's rotation, and therefore well before the very earliest fossils we know here on Earth and thus at the very beginning of its decipherable geologic history.

## Meteor Craters on the Earth

But if the Moon was thus bombarded by so many huge meteors and asteroid bodies, why do we find nothing comparable on the surface of the Earth? After all, the Earth's mass is 81 times as great, its surface gravity six times that of the Moon, and it should therefore have attracted even more bodies, and these falling at higher velocities. Yet we find here only a few identifiable meteor craters, and those few of relatively insignificant sizes. The largest, only recently discovered, is the Chubb Crater in northern Quebec, only two miles in diameter but a quarter-mile in depth. The best known is the Coon Butte Crater near Flagstaff, Arizona, less than a mile across. There are some small craters near Haviland, Kansas; others near Odessa, Texas; at least six on the Esthonian island of Oesel in the Baltic; a group near Henbury in central Australia and two at Wabar on the Persian Gulf Coast of Arabia. Also there were large meteor falls in central Siberia in 1908 and near Vladivostok in 1947.

Baldwin also lists a dozen geologically ancient formations which he describes as "fossil meteor craters." They are all found in well exposed bedrock, not greatly folded, which shows the explosive, but nonvolcanic, disruption characteristic of meteor craters. They range in age from Miocene (say 15 million years) to Late Cambrian (about 450 million years) and have therefore been subjected to agelong denudation, burial, and other geologic destruction until their true nature is often doubtful. They include, in approximate order of increasing age, the following formations:

SUSPECTED "FOSSIL" METEOR CRATERS

| Name and Location | Geologic Age | Miles Across |
|---|---|---|
| Steinham Basin, southern Germany | Miocene | 1½ |
| Rieskessel, Germany | Miocene | 15 |
| Sierra Madera, western Texas | Cretaceous | 3 |
| Upheaval Dome, Utah | Jurassic | 3 |
| Wells Creek, Tennessee | Mississippian | 6 |
| Flynn Creek, Tennessee | Dev. or Miss. | 2 |
| Vredeport Dome, Orange Free State | Devonian | 75 |
| Serpent Mound, Ohio | Devonian | 4 |
| Jeptha Knob, Tennessee | Silurian | 2 |
| Kentland, Indiana | Ordovician | ? |
| Howell, Tennessee | Ordovician | 1 |
| Decaturville, Missouri | Cambrian | ? |

Note the large diameters of the Vredeport and Rieskessel formations, truly comparable to large lunar crater dimensions. Recently, United States government geologists have confirmed the meteoric origin of the Sierra Madera in western Texas, describing its shatter cone formation as due to an *asteroid* fall some seventy or more million years ago. To this list should probably be added a group of suspected meteoric *bays* on the coastal plain of the Carolinas, Virginia, and Georgia, best seen in aerial photographs. Baldwin even adds as possibly meteoric the green *maria* observed on the planet Mars, and perhaps its smaller dark spots called *oases*, which may well be sunken meteoric craters which trap water and so sustain vegetation. On Mercury too, he points out that the dark areas look like lunar *maria*, and may be due to the infall of bodies of asteroid size.

Obviously the Earth's meteor craters rarely compare in size, and certainly not in numbers, with those dominating the land-scape of the Moon. The overwhelming reason for this is un-doubtedly the existence of an atmosphere and surface waters on the Earth, but not on the Moon. For one thing, the Earth's atmosphere acts as a protective shield which, by resistance and friction, slows up the landing speeds of meteors and burns up all but the largest and slowest moving. Furthermore, an at-mosphere and surface waters result in effective, constant, and agelong erosion of land surfaces and therefore tend to destroy superficial meteor-made craters of any considerable age. It is evident that even the Moon's latest important craters are prob-ably a billion or more years old, with meteoric bombardment and crater formation becoming inconsequential since then. This must have been true also for the Earth itself, where for all that time the erasure of visible craters must have been going on steadily. All the Earth's obvious meteoric craters are therefore probably less than a hundred thousand years old, which is merely yesterday on the long geologic calendar.

The Moon, on the other hand, has neither atmosphere to shield nor surface waters to erode. They have been lost, either by dispersion into space because the Moon's slight surface gravity could not hold them, or by chemical combination or by absorption into the lunar rocks. Consequently there has been practically no erosion to wear away the crater forms, and we see our Moon virtually as it was a billion or so years ago. Shrinkage and expansion by rapid cooling and heating must have disintegrated surface rocks to form talus at the bases of steep slopes and a widespread cover of rubble and dust, but has made little impress on the bolder contours which we can see. Change in the Moon is therefore slow, hardly to be expected unless some unusually large meteoric body strays too near and strikes, probably a most infrequent event.

### Does the Moon Surface Change?

Nevertheless, several astronomers, quite contrary to prevailing opinion, still definitely and persistently insist that the Moon's surface does change. Significantly, they are largely those who spend much time watching the Moon, looking for changes. Those changes admittedly occur only here and there in small, elusive, and usually temporary details. Sometimes there is a clouding over of familiar markings within a crater as if a gaseous fog had hidden them. Or perhaps, as the lunar day progresses, there is an unusual change in the faint color hues which only the alert and trained observer can see. Such changes are often too transitory to be caught by photography (even with our giant telescopes), and can be detected only by the zealously patient Moon observer who maintains constant telescopic watch by eye and so comes to know every minute feature as it appears from moment to moment with each progressive change of phase and illumination.

Only rarely, however, is a permanent change recorded. One such was the crater Linne', several miles in diameter, which was repeatedly seen by earlier observers, and then, sometime between 1843 and 1866, shrank to a small crater less than a mile across, apparently capped by a variable white halo which shrinks each time the temperature rises.

While these observers have not been actually silent, the scattered reports of their findings have not seemed impressive and convincing. Now, however, one of their number, the British astronomer V. A. Firsoff, has provided an imposing overall account in his current book, *Strange World of the Moon*. But he does even better by suggesting certain revisions of Moon theory based largely upon such observed surface changes.

He points out that the high scorching temperatures we ascribe (and measure) at lunar midday, are actually limited to level areas near the equator, and elsewhere on mountain slopes directly facing the Sun. Otherwise the Sun's rays fall slantwise and are spread out over more surface, so that temperatures are much lower, falling well below the freezing point of water near the poles and wherever there is total shadow. In fact there are spots in some craters of high latitudes where the Sun never shines, and snow and ice can remain permanently. All this, he concludes, means that there are also some spots where lowly and specially adapted forms of life can exist and survive.

### Frozen Sub-surface Skin

Furthermore, a few feet below the pumice-like or powdery surface, the temperature is probably always well below freezing, and the sub-soil therefore consolidated by a deep layer of ice into a continuously solid crust. This agrees with the recent report by Thomas Gold of a sub-surface ice layer, though Gold places it much deeper under the surface. Firsoff thinks that the rocks of this sub-surface are highly porous, due partly to the low surface gravity and therefore low pressures of consolidation. But also he thinks them due to past upward movements through them of gases released by chemical reactions and by radioactive heating of the interior.

Such a deep sub-surface skin of porous rocks and powdery soil, consolidated by freezing of the included water, may be the explanation for the huge lunar craters. Deeper in the interior, radioactivity is slowly heating up lavas mixed with volcanic gases. Both the gases and the lavas (lightened by heat expansion) work their way upward toward the surface, the gases more readily and rapidly. If the gases find openings for exit, they may spread out as low-lying fogs temporarily hiding familiar surface markings, or reveal themselves merely by slight changes in coloration. If the hot lavas also find exits, or manage to melt or force their way through the frozen sub-surface, then they will flow and spread out as flat plains, small or large as the topography and volume or fluidity of the lavas determine. Or the interior heat may merely melt local areas of the frozen sub-soil into fluid mud which will also flow out into flat plains.

If, however, the rising gases or lavas cannot find or force exits through the frozen skin-layer, their pressures may often cause uplift of that layer here and there as great surface blisters. Firsoff calls attention to some Moon formations which look like such blisters still intact. But with increasing uplift pressures, or eventual melting through, such blisters may burst, and according to Firsoff, should then result in the familiar lunar craters. But it is not clear how the mechanism of blister formation and bursting should actually produce the characteristic forms of these craters. Also it must be inferred from this general theory of gases and lavas escaping from the interior in large volume, that the Moon must have shrunken considerably in bulk (which Firsoff recognizes) and this should have resulted in much surface folding, rather than fracturing, which is quite contrary to present appearance.

According to Gordon J. F. MacDonald of the National Aeronautics and Space Agency, reporting on recent data gathered by our Vanguard satellites, the Moon has not been shrinking appreciably during its career, is strongly rigid as evidenced by its holding its gravitationally unbalanced figure, and is probably less dense within its interior and more dense near the surface, due to the outside accumulation of heavier meteoric matter. From a careful re-study of the whole problem of its dynamic history, he concludes that the Moon is less than one and a half billion years old, and was probably originally a small planet captured by too close passing of the Earth.

### Puzzle of the Crater Rays

One major feature of lunar topography still remains altogether puzzling, that of the conspicuous white rays which radiate from certain craters (notably Tycho), best seen at full moon as in Plate XX. Firsoff objects to the theory that meteor impact explosions threw out streams of finely powdered material to form these rays. One objection is that some rays are clearly tangental to the crater rim, which they should not be if projected outward by a central explosion. Less convincing is his other objection that the ray material was often apparently obstructed by low obstacles, being thin or absent to the lee of such obstacles. But is this not precisely what should happen with material projected violently outward from an explosion? First, the obstruction is exactly as it should be if the directions of movement were outward. And second, such material orbiting roughly parallel to the Moon surface, could and would be intercepted by upraised obstacles as it came down to landings at low angles.

Firsoff mentions other theories of the rays as well, while leaving the whole problem quite open. Among these is the idea offered by William H. Pickering in 1903, that the rays are due to electrostatic repulsions spreading their white materials radially. Another idea is that of H. P. Wilkins, as recent as 1954, who finds that rays emerging over the north curvature of the Moon can be prolonged to another center directly opposite to Tycho (which he therefore calls "Anti-Tycho"), suggesting that these two are the Moon's magnetic poles, with the rays somehow due to magnetic lines of force. Of all the theories, however, that of meteoric explosion seems at present the most realistic. But also it must be fairly said that so far the evidence is in no way decisive, and may not become so until our astronauts step out of their rocket capsules to make a first-hand study of the lunar ground.

CHAPTER **8**

EARTH'S NETHER REGIONS

In order to go on now with our story of the Earth itself, we must somehow probe into its nether regions. For even its surface history must depend in large part on what is going on more deeply down below. Most of what we know factually of its recorded past is just such surface history, which (for reasons to appear) we more and more suspect is rather effect than cause.

In a previous chapter we did refer to the Earth's dense core and several overlying shells of rock. But how can we know about these? For certainly we have not been deep enough inside to learn about them firsthand. If the Earth were an orange in size, our deepest borings in wells and mines would take us through only a thin sheet of tissue paper on its surface. And even Nature's own diggings, by cutting deep river gorges and generally eroding away overlying surface layers, have not taken us much deeper. Then how can we really know what is deep below, say in the very core itself?

One important clue is found in the average density of the Earth as a whole. This we arrive at by weighing the Earth, then dividing by its volume, which we know very exactly because we have measured its size (diameter, circumference, etc.) very precisely. But first, of course, we must somehow weigh the Earth, and what scales have we for doing that?

### Weighing the Earth

Theoretically, weighing the Earth is easy, but in practice it is exceedingly difficult. Theoretically it is done simply by measuring the gravitational pull of a relatively small body of known weight, and comparing that with the known pull of the Earth itself. However, we must take into consideration the respective distances between the centers of pull, which in the case of the Earth is the distance from center to surface, or its radius of about four thousand miles.

The first relatively small object used in guessing the mass of the Earth was the mountain Chimborazo in Ecuador, but as its real weight could only be roughly estimated, the result was most uncertain. To overcome this, the English astronomer Nevil Maskelyne in 1774 attempted to weigh the Scotch mountain Schiehallion. This narrow east-west ridge was first carefully surveyed to get its exact volume. Then borings were made for sampling its materials to estimate its weight. Finally plumb bobs were hung up on each side and the deflections of the plumb lines from the vertical carefully measured to determine the gravitational pull of the mountain mass. This was then compared with the Earth-pull, with the respective distances of pull taken into account. The result, we know now, came out about 20 per cent too low, for reasons which were not then understood.

The more modern method was proposed and first used as early as 1789 by Lord Henry Cavendish, but made precise only recently. You cannot weigh a mountain at all exactly, nor bring it into the laboratory, and there are other upsetting factors. But you can substitute a couple of very heavy weights to deflect a couple of small weights against a very slight, but known, resistance. For example, you can balance the small weights at the ends of a horizontal rod suspended at its middle by a fine fiber. The only resistance is the twist in the fiber, so the device is really very sensitive. With it, for instance, Paul R. Heyl of the United States Bureau of Standards, determined

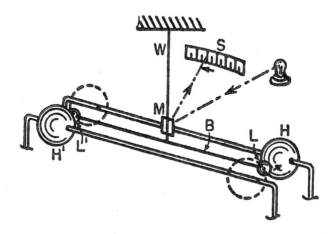

*Figure 13. Cavendish Method of Weighing Earth*

Two lightweight balls L and L' at ends of bar B, suspended by a thin wire W having a mirror M reflecting a light beam from a lamp to scale S. Heavyweight balls H and H' pull ball L and L' gravitationally a slight distance against the twist resistance of wire W, turning the mirror and the position of the light beam on scale S. Comparing this pull with that of the Earth gives the weight of the Earth.

the mass of the Earth to be 6600 billion billion tons, the figure now accepted by the scientific world, with an estimated accuracy within one part in a thousand.

That figure is a very basic one, being used in a lot of other mass determinations. From it, for example, we get the masses of the Moon, planets, and Sun, and in a few cases the stars. Thus with it we can weigh the Moon. For the Earth and the Moon are gravitational dancing partners who swing each other around once a month at a known distance apart, from which we can figure their combined mass. Also they swing each other about a common center of gravity, the Moon in a large orbit, the Earth in a small one. Precise astronomical observations then tell how the Earth itself moves about this center of gravity, which proves to be well within the Earth, 2880 miles from its center. From this the astronomers get the relative masses of the Earth and Moon (81.56 to 1), and so easily the weight and density of the Moon as well as the Earth. The Earth's density proves to be 5.52 times that of water, a very important figure. As to the Moon's density, that too is easily derived from its volume and mass; it is 3.34 times that of water.

### The Earth's Interior

Going one step further in our probing into the Earth's nether regions, how is that mass of the Earth distributed in depth? When we weigh representative samples of the accessible crustal rocks, we get a density of only 2.65 for the granitic rocks of the continents, and about 2.85 for the underlying basalts, with a rough average of about 2.75 for the crust as a whole. Obviously, to average out at 5.52 for the Earth as a whole, the core material must be of much greater density, which agrees rather well with iron (density 7.9), nickel (8.9), and other heavy metals. We have long suspected a predominantly iron-nickel core because the Earth acts as a giant magnet, and these are the important magnetic elements. Be that as it may, we can still be quite sure that the deep materials of the Earth are heavy, the surface materials light.

Nearly two centuries ago, Laplace even figured out on theoretical grounds just how the Earth densities should vary as we proceed toward the center. At the surface the density should be 2.72 times that of water, which agrees closely with our crust samplings; 1000 miles down, 5.62; 2000 miles down, 8.30; 3000 miles down, 10.19; and at the center, 10.87. Furthermore, we can figure how the Earth should behave as to certain astronomic movements such as precession wobble, with its matter thus distributed. The actual behavior turns out to correspond with theory, but unfortunately this is not really decisive, as other possible distributions might do the same.

You may have noticed that the big relative increases in density occur not near the center, but toward the surface. That is because gravity itself decreases with depth, becoming nothing at all at the very center, where all the gravity-pulls of the Earth's mass exactly balance each other. But that does not mean that the central pressures are not greater, for they depend on the weights of the overlying masses. In fact, at the very center they are greatest, one good guess being over twenty thousand tons per square inch. This is enough, as indicated by much more modest laboratory pressure tests, to make matter act very queerly by surface standards. Such pressures should make all substances very stiff, yet cause them to flow almost like water. So things must really be very different down there, and we obviously need more than mere theory to probe effectively into the Earth's interior.

### Probing by Earthquakes

Such a probe is provided by earthquakes. An earthquake originates somewhere within the body of the Earth and is probably due to a sudden shift of rocks giving way to an accumulating pressure or other strain. Because of the great masses involved and the suddenness of the shifts, severe tremors are sent out as waves throughout the Earth mass and can be recorded by sensitive instruments called "seismographs" suitably placed over the surface of the Earth. These draw wiggly lines on moving tapes to show movements in the various directions. By comparing such records picked up and carefully timed at points far apart on the Earth, we determine the point of origin of an earthquake, its depth below the surface, and, very important, the speeds and directions at which the various tremor waves travel. For there are several kinds of waves, and they follow different paths. Some are compressional, like sound waves, and will go through anything, solid or fluid, but faster through denser materials. Others are distortional waves which are carried only by solids and are therefore stopped by anything fluid. Some travel the short way nearly straight through the Earth's depths, others take curved surface routes. Put them all together, they tell the experts that the Earth core is about 4300 miles in diameter, and so dense it accounts for one-third of the whole Earth mass, though its volume is only one-sixth. Oddly enough, this core acts like a fluid (such as molten metal) in stopping the distortional earthquake waves, but has nevertheless great rigidity because of the enormous pressures of the heavy overlying rocks. These rocks make up a thick mantle of somewhat uncertain composition comprising nearly all of the remaining two-thirds mass. Then at the Earth's surface are two very thin layers of low-density rocks, basaltic below, granitic above, making up the unstably solid crust on which we live.

Because digging is hard work, man has never penetrated very deeply into even the Earth's crust. Of course there are thousands of mine shafts and well borings which we think of as deep, but actually they only prick the skin, as it were. However, there is a tantalizingly mysterious change where the crust and mantle meet, named the Mohorovicic Discontinuity after

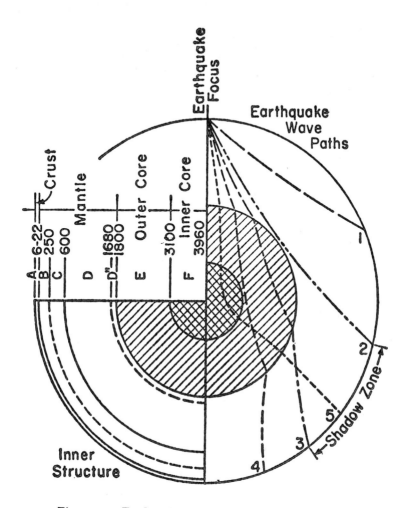

*Figure 14.  Earthquake Probing of the Earth's Interior*

Tremor waves from an earthquake focus travel through the Earth along paths curving with changing density. Points and times of emergence indicate an iron-nickel core (the inner part solid, the outer part fluid), surrounded by a stony mantle of several layers, and a thin outer crust of basalts and granites. (After R. Paul Larkin, in *How Old Is The Earth?* by Patrick M. Hurley, Doubleday, 1959.)

the Croatian seismologist who discovered it in 1909, and in a couple of ocean spots the crust has been found to be very thin (at one spot only three miles). One site is a couple of hundred miles north of Puerto Rico; the other is off the Pacific Coast of northern Mexico. A committee of the National Academy of Sciences and the National Research Council is planning the boring of a "Mohole" right through the crust to solve the mysteries of the transition to and composition of the mantle underneath.

### The Interior Heat

Our borings to date, however, have revealed at least one significant fact, that the deeper we go, the hotter it gets. Under tropical desert or polar snow, whatever the surface temperature may be, a short way down everything is uniformly warm, and with increasing depth, grows ever hotter. The rate of increase is quite steady, about 16 degrees Fahrenheit for each thousand feet. At that rate, the temperature a mile and a half down should be at the boiling point of water, and beginning about 30 miles down, hot enough to melt at least the basalts of the Earth-crust. If this rate of increase continues, the center of the Earth may have a temperature of ten thousand degrees, though some recent investigators have questioned such high central temperatures.

For the present, however, we are mainly concerned with those melting temperatures at the bottom of the Earth-crust, for they (plus the Moon) are apparently the keys to the story of our ever changing home here on the Earth's surface. Such temperatures indicate the solid crust of the continents and ocean basins are relatively thin, and *floating*. The substratum of basaltic rocks on which the solid crust rests must be capable of yielding and flowing under the heavy pressures, heat, and other forces, even though thickly and with strong resistance.

### Crust in Floating Balance

If the crustal rocks are thus actually afloat, we may safely infer a very important result—that the continental rocks are lighter since they float high, and the rocks of the ocean basins heavier since they float low in the substratum. For the same general reason, we may properly assume that where high mountain masses protrude above the general continental level, to float so high the material under them must be lighter stuff and extend more deeply down into the supporting substratum. In other words, a world-wide balance of flotation is maintained, giving the entire crust a general stability rather remarkable in view of its relative thinness and great irregularity.

This theory of balanced flotation is named *isostasy*, and was arrived at by first discovering the fact that mountain masses are actually lighter than expected, one example being the mountain Schiehallion, used in weighing the Earth. The discovery was actually made, however, when a century ago, a triangulation survey of northern India was undertaken just south of the Great Massif of the Himalaya Mountains. It was found that the survey measurements did not agree with the astronomical determinations of latitude, which employed a plumb line. It was at once inferred that the gravitational pull of the nearby mountain mass drew the plumb line out of vertical, and so upset the astronomical sightings. Estimating the mass of the mountains, it was calculated what the pull on the plumb bob should be, and then discovered that the actual pull was only a third of the expected amount. Thereupon, Sir

George B. Airy, Astronomer Royal of England, suggested that the lighter crustal rocks of the mountain mass extended deeper into the heavy lavas underneath and therefore floated higher to form the mountains. This conclusion has since been fully confirmed by extensive and precise gravity measurements conducted by (among many others) the United States Geodetic Survey. It has led to a general understanding of the basic manner in which the great elevations and depressions of the Earth's surface are formed and maintained by balanced flotation on the denser and somewhat yielding substratum of basaltic lavas.

Is the basaltic substratum actually fluid, and therefore very yielding? Or is it quite solid, and only slightly and slowly yielding? That probably depends on temperatures and pressures, and it can be tested.

### The Earth-Tides

The test concerns tides in the Earth-crust itself. If the substratum is fluid and flows easily, there should be strong tides in it twice daily. These should be comparable to the ocean tides, which should then be hardly noticeable at all, for the same reason one does not notice them from a boat out at sea. In other words, the ocean and crust tides would rise and fall together. So the fact that we do see the ocean tides rise and fall along the coasts must mean that there are no comparable movements of the continents, arguing against a fluid substratum.

However, a classic experiment by the physicists Albert A. Michelson and Henry G. Gale did demonstrate a tide in the body of the Earth itself, but less than a third that of the oceans, averaging only 14 inches up and down. But it is not a flow tide in a fluid substratum, but rather an elastic deformation in the solid globe as a whole, which, as confirmed by earthquake studies, is as rigid (and elastic) as steel. This tide is real enough, but so smooth we never feel it. So we conclude that the substratum, at least now, is substantially solid. But we also know that it must yield to strong continued pressures, otherwise the continents would not be in balanced flotation upon it. In short, it acts like beeswax; though solid, it is also slowly plastic.

From this rigidity we must conclude that the temperature of the substratum is low enough, and the pressure on it heavy enough, to keep it from melting to fluidity. Perhaps, without that pressure, it would really melt. We are not sure. But suppose the temperature were to rise, what then would happen?

### Overheating the Substratum

In 1923, the eminent Professor John Joly of Trinity College, Dublin University, gave a most illuminating lecture before the Geological Society of London in which he assumed just that, and followed it in 1925 with a classic book on *The Surface History of the Earth*, based on just such a temperature rise. He began by pointing out that the granites and basalts of the Earth's crust are known to contain the radioactive elements thorium and uranium. We know that in their normal breakdown they release heat slowly, and Joly showed that this heat was being released faster than it could escape at the surface of the continents. In other words, the continents act as blankets to keep the heat in. Consequently the heat must accumulate and the substratum temperatures therefore slowly rise, with the higher temperatures at the greater depths, just as we find them to be.

At least that is how it would be under the continents. Under the oceans things were probably somewhat different. The crust there is thinner, so the heat can escape more readily to the sea bottom. There the very cold waters pick up the heat and soon carry it to the surface where it is quickly lost. And yet it may not always escape fast enough, so even under oceans the substratum temperatures may be rising, though much more slowly.

Let all this go on long enough (say some tens of millions of years), and the basaltic substratum, especially under the continents, must get hot enough to melt despite all overlying pressures. Several things should then properly happen.

### Sinking Continents

First, as the basalts melt, they expand, probably about 10 to 12 per cent. But such expansion means reduction in density, and that reduces the flotation power. In other words, as the substratum expands, the continents must actually sink deeper into it to reach flotation balance. The net result is a lowering of the land areas relative to the levels of the oceans, which rest largely on thin basaltic bottoms. This must cause a general flooding of all low-lying areas by transgressing shallow seas, covering all coastal lowlands and lower levels of inland plains, deserts, and valleys. This is in exact accord with the geologic record, which shows that from 50 to 80 per cent of the land areas have from time to time in the past been thus submerged beneath shallow encroaching seas.

Meanwhile, we must not forget, the familiar processes of weathering and erosion would be going on. From every ocean, sea, and lake, moisture would be evaporated by the Sun's heat, carried by winds over the land areas, and there precipi-

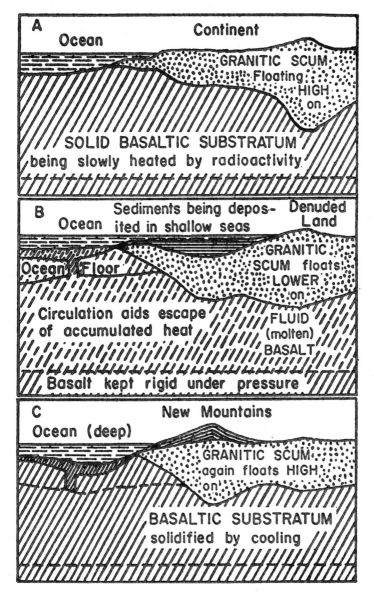

Figure 15. Joly's Theory of Crustal Cycle

tated as rain or snow. The waters running down every mountain and lesser slope would remove the soil and carry it off to the lakes and seas, and there spread it out more or less flatly over the bottoms as layers of sand or mud. Eventually, as the ages passed, these stratified layers would accumulate, and by cementing, heat, and pressure, become solidified and often hardened into our familiar sedimentary rocks.

As the sediments thus accumulated over the bottoms of the shallow lakes and seas, their increasing weight would force the underlying crust deeper into the fluid substratum, thus making room for more layers to be added. Keeping in mind that at least under the shallow continental seas the granite crust must have been thin, this yielding to the increasing weight was quite inevitable, permitting very deep deposits to accumulate as the millions of years went by.

On the other hand, as the mountains and other elevated areas were cut down by slow erosion, their reduced weight permitted their flotational uplift. As they were already supported by low-density granitic masses greatly thickened downward, such uplifting was also inevitable, thereby providing long continuing uplifts supplying the erosion materials for piling up the deep deposits in the shallow seas.

A second general effect of substratum heating, melting, and expansion would be a small, but significant, increase in the Earth's dimensions. Joly estimated the average substratum thickness at sixty miles or more. Then a 10 or 12 per cent expansion by melting should increase its thickness by six or seven miles, the diameter of the Earth by twice that much, and its circumference by about forty miles. Recent estimates are somewhat smaller, but in any case this means a stretching of the still solid surface of the crust, so that cracks appear, only to be filled in immediately by molten lavas from below which quickly cooled. If ever the substratum later cools, solidifies,

Plate XI. CORONA OF THE SUN. Photo taken during totality of solar eclipse of June 8, 1918, at Green River, Wyoming. Rayed appearance suggests strong electromagnetic and radiation forces. (Mount Wilson and Palomar Observatories.)

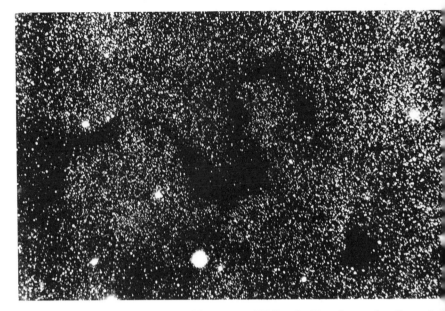

*Plate XIII.* Variable Nebula in Monoceros. NGC 2261. Two photos taken Septembe[r] 18, 1920, and November 1, 1921, showing irregular variability. Though apparently illu[m-] minated by nearby variable star (spectra alike), the variations seem oddly unconnected (Mount Wilson and Palomar Observatories.)

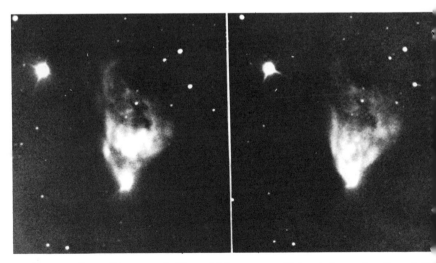

*Plate XII.* Dark "Elephant's Trunk" Nebulosity. Not a dark opening through th[e] star field, but a winding cool opaque cloud of obscuring dust, perhaps compressed [by] hotter transparent gas about it. (Mount Wilson and Palomar Observatories.)

*Plate XIV.* GLOBULAR CLUSTER IN HERCULES. M 13. NGC 6205. Visible to naked eye and revealed by a small telescope as a compact globular star cluster typical of approximately one hundred connected with the Milky Way system. It probably contains about one hundred thousand stars. (Mount Wilson and Palomar Observatories.)

*Plate XV.* PLEIADES CLUSTER AND NEBULOSITY. M 45. Open star cluster in Taurus, the main stars separable by naked eye, which also sees hazy nebulosity, here becoming visible with short photo exposure. Longer exposure discloses strong nebulosity throughout the cluster. (Mount Wilson and Palomar Observatories.)

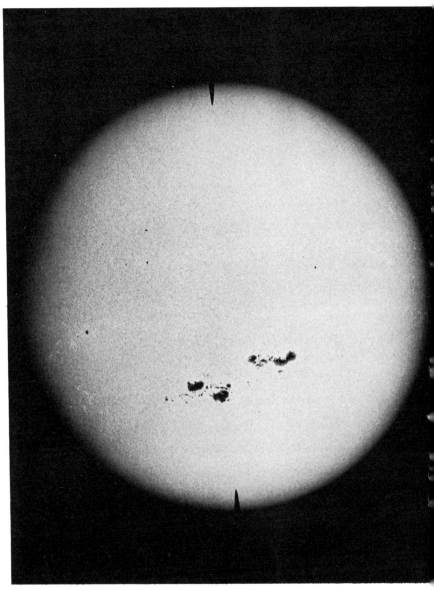

*Plate XVI.* SOLAR DISC WITH SUN-SPOTS. Photo of Sun July 31, 1949, showing group of large sun-spots and the fine structure of surface. Spots are huge cyclonic storms. (Mount Wilson and Palomar Observatories.)

and shrinks as a whole, this enlarged surface crust must prove too big and so wrinkle considerably to fit the reduced size of the Earth.

### Cooling Substratum

But what could bring about such substratum cooling? Joly's answer follows from another long-period effect of substratum melting and liquifying, namely a general shifting of the continents over the surface of the overheated substratum. For one thing, with melting of the substratum, real tides would begin within it, with a consequent general flow toward the west, carrying the floating continents with it. Also, and here important, the tidal pull on them would be just a little greater, tending to hurry them forward faster. All this would be helped by the freeing of the continental roots from the earlier anchorages in solid substratum. They would be like icebergs, originally landlocked, but now afloat and free to travel along any current and in response to any pull, tidal or otherwise. Of course, even the melted substratum would be only thickly fluid, flowing but stiffly, and still resisting somewhat any drift through it. In this respect, it would be like molasses rather than water.

Besides the tendency of the continents to drift westward under tidal pull, they would also tend to drift from the poles toward the equator. Again it would be because they protrude above the general surface level, being thereby a bit more subject to the combination of tidal pull and centrifugal force, both drawing them away from the Earth's axis and toward the equator.

Given some tens of millions of years, such slow drifting of

the continents relative to the substratum would have a most important result, the uncovering of those areas of substratum which had been overheated under the continents. In other words, the heat-retaining blankets would have been drawn aside, and a period of substratum cooling and resolidifying would set in. The result would be shrinkage, reduction of the Earth's diameter, and an inevitable wrinkling of the surface crust to fit a smaller Earth.

## Wrinkling Earth-Crust

Where would such wrinkling be most likely to occur? Probably in the thinner and weaker areas of the Earth-crust. Broadly, these are the ocean basins and the lower parts of the continents. In the ocean basins, downward folding seems to prevail, producing the great ocean deeps, and probably controlled by the predominant cooling and general shrinkage going on there. On the other hand, the crust under the transgressional seas seems most subject to folding, being not only thinner, but because of the presence of recently deposited and incompletely consolidated sedimentary strata, also structurally weaker. Here foldings then produce mountain ranges, but these too are predominantly downfolds thickening the granite crust and pressing deeper into the underlying basaltic magmas, thus gaining flotational support for the smaller upper portions of the folds uplifted at the surface as the visible mountains.

Another factor determining positions of mountain ranges is undoubtedly the necessity of wrinkling the crust to fit in both length and breadth, east-west as well as north-south. The reason is of course that the substratum shrinkage reduces the Earth's circumference in all directions. On the whole, the mountains of the Americas are thought of as providing the east-west fitting, those of southern Europe and Asia the north-south fitting.

## The Crustal Cycle

But mountain-building does not depend on crustal buckling alone. As the substratum basalts cooled, their shrinkage and solidifying increased their density and therefore flotational power. The result would be a strong uplift of those mountain areas already thickened by folding, and of course a lesser uplift of the thinner unfolded areas. Thus the mountains would be raised even higher above the continental lowlands, and the lowlands themselves would be lifted above sea level, so the shallow transgressional seas would retire from the continents. Also, with the substratum solidified, the granitic continents would be more firmly anchored and thus stopped from rapid drifting. Then again they would act as blankets retaining accumulating radioactive heat until, after some tens of millions of years, substratum overheating and melting would start another great cycle of crustal changes.

Study of the geologic record shows very plainly that this fundamental cycle has recurred again and again. Eras much like our own in crustal stability have been followed by continental sinking and invasion by shallow seas in which deep sedimentary strata were slowly laid down. These sea-bottom deposits were later crumpled and uplifted into great mountain chains, only to be later worn down in large part by long continuing erosion. During the periods of deposition, the fossil remains of life forms were preserved to give us a fairly orderly and progressive record of evolutionary development, only to be interrupted and largely destroyed during the ensuing periods of mountain-building and erosion. Thus the great eras of recorded geologic history are marked by their characteristic fossil remains embedded in stratified deposits. On the other hand, the periods of mountain-building are notably interruptions, described by the geologists as *Revolutions*, each named by some great mountain range it produced. A summary of this cyclical history is given in the concluding chapter.

In nearly all this, the Moon had a vital part. For it would undoubtedly be greatly responsible for the tidal shifting of the Earth's continents and particularly effective during periods of substratum melting, thus drawing aside the granitic blankets causing overheating, thus permitting cooling and all else that followed cyclically. In contrast, the planet Mars, with only insignificant moons, would lack such strong tides—probably a contributing reason for its apparent lack of mountains.

### No Moon Cycle

Also our Moon bears upon its face the evidence that it did not enjoy such a cycle of surface changes. Whatever its early surface history may have been, the rapid slowing of its rotation period reduced any tides within it to inconsequence. Its low density, only 3.34 times that of water, means that it is composed of lighter rock packed less tightly, perhaps mostly basalt and granite if it really was born of the Earth-crust. Its surface area compared with its mass is about six times that of the Earth, making its general cooling much easier and more rapid. Although it undoubtedly has its share of radioactive minerals, and so its continuous generation of radioactive heat, it apparently has no continental masses floating on a general substratum of denser, but plastic, materials, and therefore no large-scale horizontal shifting of surface areas. If here and there pockets of over-heating, melting, and expanding materials should accumulate, there would be no release except by upward flowage of those materials themselves. In some cases, such release may have been by quiet outflow to the surface through existing fissures, producing wide level plains of frozen lava, another obvious explanation of the so-called *maria* or seas. In other cases, pent-up volcanic forces may find no release other than violent explosions producing craters. These may, however, start as crustal blisters contained by a frozen sub-surface layer which finally melts and bursts to form the crater shapes. As surface gravity is one-sixth that on Earth, the resulting craters might run larger than those here on Earth, perhaps even to the hugeness of many that we observe on the Moon's scarred face. So it may be, when we can visit the Moon and study its surface features more closely, that we will find that both volcanic action and meteoric falls have played their parts in the disfigurement of the Moon's face.

But let us get back to Earth. In this present day of scientific attitude and inquiry, we are for the first time gaining a realization of what is actually happening about us, and find that we are living on an Earth-crust of relative stability, but also of great potential change. Whatever ultimate threat the Nether Regions may hold for us, it will probably come only after some tens of millions of years of slow radioactive internal heating. Then we may well expect the day of melting substratum, sinking lands, and flooding by shallow seas, continents loosely afloat in a thickly fluid medium, carried by tidal currents and hurried by more direct tidal pulls to drift and turn rather chaotically over the face of the Earth. Then our distant descendants will really know what crustal instability can mean.

# CHAPTER 9

## ARE THE CONTINENTS ADRIFT?

Do you remember the old-time Chinese laundry ticket? You brought your wash. Then the laundryman marked a piece of paper with one of those mysterious crows-feet he used for writing. Then he tore the paper across, handed you one piece and kept the other himself. When you came back, he fitted the torn edge of your piece against the edge of his, and made sure also that the two halves of the crows-foot fitted together. If they did fit, he knew that you and the laundry belonged together.

On the map of the world is just such a Chinese laundry ticket. You see it best on a world globe. On the two sides of the southern Atlantic, notice how closely the coasts of Africa and South America would fit each other if shoved together. Even the minor bulges on one fit into the indentations on the other. It looks as if they had been torn apart and separated by three thousand miles. Already, back in the seventeenth century, Sir Francis Bacon had noticed the close fit, even on the crude maps resulting from the then recent early explorations, and guessed that the continents had split and drifted apart. That guess was repeated by Buffon in the next century on the same grounds. The theory was finally made more positive by the astronomer William H. Pickering (1907) and by the

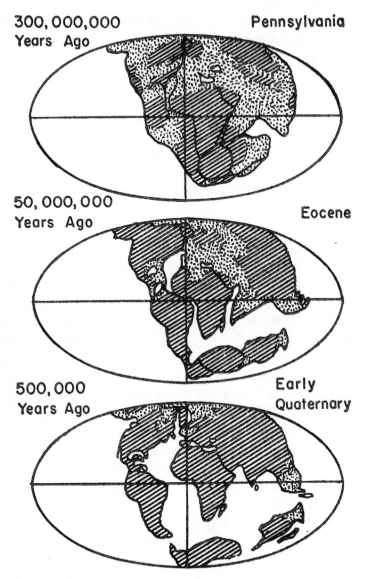

300,000,000 Years Ago     Pennsylvania

50,000,000 Years Ago     Eocene

500,000 Years Ago     Early Quaternary

*Figure 16. Wegener's Maps of Continental Drifting*

(Reproduced from *The Origin of Continents and Oceans*, by Alfred Wegener, by permission of Methuen & Co., Ltd., and E. P. Dutton & Co., Inc.)

geologists F. B. Taylor (1910) and Alfred Wegener (1912). They even fitted Europe and North America together, with Greenland, Iceland, and the British Isles in between like a puzzle of many pieces instead of a simple laundry ticket of just two. The fit was fairly close.

By 1922, Wegener had developed the theory in detail and gathered a formidable array of evidence for it, all of which he presented in his classic work *The Origin of Continents and Oceans*. Much has of course been added since by others, and we will here consider the evidence as now accumulated.

### Evidence from Geographic Features

Wegener began, in effect, by studying the crows-feet on the two sides of the Atlantic, the conspicuous geologic features, to see if they too would fit. Many of them did. For instance, South Africa and South America have ancient mountain ranges of the same geologic age, running in the same directions and fitting closely when the continents are brought together. Paralleling these are a series of troughs, collectively known as the *Samfrau Graben*, a German abbreviation of South America-Africa-Australia, because they now extend across all three of these separated continents. Along these troughs are found equivalent geologic strata, mineral ores, and deposits, such as diamonds in Brazil and South Africa, and notably gold, as in Peru, South Africa, and the deserts of Australia.

The crows-feet on the opposing, but now dismembered, shores of the North Atlantic are almost as convincing in their apparent ancient continuity. Our Appalachian Mountains are continued in Scandinavia, while those of Nova Scotia and Newfoundland are of the same age, direction, and rock formations as those of the British Isles. Pennsylvania's coal measures extend through New England and Nova Scotia to fit those of the British Isles, Central Europe, and Southern Russia.

We have discovered another revealing fact: that there actually was a mountain country just east of North America where the Atlantic Ocean now lies. When rivers carry the rock and soil materials from mountains or other high lands down into the sea, they drop the coarse gravels near the shore, the sand farther out, and the finer silts even farther. So we can tell from such ancient sea bottoms just which way the shore and the mountains beyond were located. In the eastern United States, the coarse deposits lie toward the east, so the mountains which supplied the material must have been there too. From the coarseness and abundance of the material, we know that those mountains were big and very near. And over in Europe, now far away, but then presumably nearby, we find the worn-down stumps of ancient mountains of just the right geologic age to supply the needed materials. And then too, the rock layers of Scotland, Scandinavia, and Finland indicate a lost land off to the northwest, which would be Greenland and northern North America if the theory of Atlantic splitting is true.

### Evidence from Distribution of Life

The present and past distributions of life forms also suggest former contacts between the Old World and the New. Thus the manatee or sea cow, which lives only in shallow warm coastal waters or river estuaries, is now found at and near the mouths of the Amazon and Congo Rivers on directly opposite sides of the Atlantic, with little likelihood that it could swim the wide ocean between them. Even more convincing, our common earthworm, which surely cannot swim the ocean, is found in both Europe and North America in limited areas, now separated, which would fit exactly if the continents were brought back together. This same explanation also applies to the present strange distribution of garden snails, pearl mussels, crabs, scorpions, spiders, fresh-water perches, mud minnows, heather, etc.

At one time the early monkeys and their primitive kin, the lemurs and tarsiers, must have traveled overland from North America to northern Africa, which they could have done with the continents in contact. In the Connecticut Valley we find the three-toed tracks of early forms of those celebrated reptiles, the dinosaurs, and exactly opposite over in southern England and Belgium, we find similar tracks. Even earlier, some of the very primitive fresh-water fishes had developed makeshift lungs. Today we have a few surviving lungfishes, but widely separated in South America, Africa, and Australia. But if those three continents were once together and then drifted apart, we readily explain this odd distribution.

Another previously mysterious fact rather strongly supports the theory. During the Carboniferous and Permian Periods about a quarter of a billion years ago, an ice sheet extended over much of Africa, South America, Australia, and India. How could ice sheets form over these areas, now warm and widely separated? Wegener held that these glaciated regions were once close together over the South Pole, so naturally there was intense cold and an ice sheet. Since then they have drifted apart and into warmer climate zones. Strongly supporting this idea is the fact that the markings left by these ancient ice sheets show that the ice generally flowed toward the north.

Wegener similarly explains our more recent Ice Age which left its marks over northern Europe and North America by assuming that the glaciated areas were then near together over the North Pole, having since drifted southward and apart.

Certainly the edges of the two ice sheets, our own following the southern New England coast, and that of Europe cutting through southern England, fit remarkably when the continents are shoved together.

### Can the Continents Drift?

But can continents drift? Are they not too firmly rooted in the solid body of the Earth? It would seem they are not. We have already learned that the continents are afloat, though not in the waters of the sea. They float in something much denser and more buoyant, in the heavier, yet yielding, rocks below them. The continents are largely composed of relatively light rocks, mostly granites, limestones, etc., while under them and under the oceans are heavier basalts. These basalts, though rigid under sudden shocks such as earthquakes, can still yield slowly under the enormous pressures which the continents impose. Molasses candy behaves like that—you can break it with a sudden snap, but also pull and bend it slowly. Consider too that the underlying layer of supporting basalt may be softened by the Earth's interior heat, and from time to time in the past, has been actually melted. So the drifting of the continents, at least during such periods of substratum melting, seems entirely possible.

But what tremendous forces can we call on to cause continental drifting? Wegener guessed that the tidal pull of the Moon on the protuberant continental masses would do it. But then Sir James H. Jeans figured it out mathematically and concluded that a tidal pull strong enough to drag the continents through the underlying basalts would have stopped the rotation of the Earth in about a year. But then, as a careful scientist, he made the broad reservation that he assumed that the existing conditions of density, stiffness, and resistance of the substratum had persisted without substantial change throughout geologic time. However, we have already discovered, there are good reasons for believing that those conditions have actually changed in the geologic past to make continental drifting quite possible, at least occasionally.

Other objections were raised against Wegener's particular theory, the most serious by the eminent geologist Charles Schuchert, of Yale University, who in 1928 held that the opposing Atlantic coast lines did not fit nearly as closely as Wegener thought. But on the other hand he objected because Africa and South America fitted too closely, considering that the sea waves had been cutting away at their coasts for millions of years since they parted company. And when it came to crows-feet, the geologic formations on the two sides of the Atlantic, they differed in so many details that he doubted the whole story, though he did admit some continental drift. However, you can cross the Hudson River from Manhattan Island to the Palisades and see as marked a difference within about a mile as Schuchert called attention to between the continents. But so impressed were the geologists of his day by his authority and objections that most of them simply closed their minds against the whole theory, some even refusing to read Wegener's book. In fact, Schuchert himself remained much more open-minded than the people he convinced.

But then how did the dissenting geologists explain those odd distributions of life on the globe, those lungfishes of South America, Africa, and Australia, for instance. By assuming ancient land bridges stretching across the oceans, from the Americas to Africa, from Africa to India and Australia, from Europe to North America. But no one has ever explained what since became of those land bridges. For instance, we should find some remnant of a long submerged ridge *across* the Atlantic from the Americas to Africa, and we do indeed find an Atlantic submarine ridge, only it runs northward and southward *parallel* to the coasts, as if a strip of torn continental edge had stuck to the bottom and got left behind when the great land masses broke and drifted apart. Similarly, the other assumed land bridges are also strangely missing.

### Great Submarine Rifts

Recently we have learned several important things about this mid-Atlantic ridge, when Dr. Maurice Ewing of Columbia University announced in 1957 that it consists of jagged mountains piled up on each side of a great crack in the sea floor, that this crack extends and branches into the other oceans of the world, and that, thus extended, it corresponds to the present belts of earthquake and volcanic activity. The main cracks are from two to five miles deep and twenty to twenty-five miles wide, and suggest a pulling apart of the sea floor as if the earth crust was being stretched. The main Atlantic crack extends northward across Iceland and the polar sea to Siberia, and southward around the end of Africa. Then it divides, one branch extending north into the Indian Ocean, finally subdividing, mostly westward into the series of rifts which extend north and south through eastern Africa and up into the Red Sea and beyond.

The other branch extends between Australia and Antarctica and then northward across the Pacific to the west coast of the United States where it comes ashore, only to return to the sea until it reaches Alaska. But just before it ends, another branch proceeds west along the Aleutian Islands. Recently the Soviet scientists have traced this branch farther southwest along the Kamchatka Peninsula and Kurile Islands to Japan. Another great crack extends along the Indonesian Islands, scene of the terrific explosion of the island volcano Krakatoa in 1883. And there are many lesser cracks which are usually connected with the main cracks so far traced. One such extends from the mid-Atlantic toward Portugal and the area of the Lisbon earthquake of 1755, and we suspect its further extension along the axis of the Mediterranean and its belt of volcanic and earthquake activity. For we have even some evidence in our historic records indicating Mediterranean crustal shifting within the brief period of Man's memory. Thus the Pillars of Hercules of the ancient Greeks are now three times farther apart on opposite sides of the Strait of Gibraltar. And the now placid channel of the two-mile-wide Strait of Messina between Sicily and the toe of Italy, when visited by Ulysses in his Odyssey, was only two-thirds as wide, and beset by the violent whirlpool of Charybdis set opposite the dangerous cliff of Scylla.

But the geologic indications of recent and current crustal shiftings are even more substantial and meaningful. The islands of the East Indies and of the West Indies would seem to be due to the breakup of continental margins. Even more certain is the evidence for the progressive breakup of the eastern half of Africa. India once belonged there, but split off as a long wedge and moved northeast until it jammed up against Asia and piled up the crumpling coasts as the great Himalaya Massif. Then the island of Madagascar split off, but so recently it has not yet traveled far. Today further cracking apart is going on, as shown by the great African Rift Valleys and their northward extensions into Asia Minor.

### Evidence of Present Drift

Also very important as evidence are the various precise observations of the latitudes and longitudes of points on the Earth's surface being made by astronomers and geographers from time to time for checking on any shifts in relative positions. For example, back in 1865, the longitude of Glasgow Observatory relative to the Royal Observatory at Greenwich was carefully determined. This was done again some seventy-two years later, with the surprising result that Glasgow had apparently drifted seven hundred feet westward, or Greenwich that same amount eastward, indicating a relative east-west movement of about ten feet per year. Quite as striking is the apparent drift of Greenland westward. In 1823, the English explorer Sir Edward Sabine discovered a small island off the northeast coast of Greenland and determined its geographic position. In 1869, Börgen and Copeland found the island nearly 1400 feet farther west, suggesting a westward drift of thirty feet per year. Then in 1907 a new determination by J. Koch showed a further drift of 3900 feet at the rate of 103 feet per year. But in 1932, Dr. H. S. Jelstrup found Sabine Island only 2000 feet west of its 1869 position, indicating a yearly westward drift of only 32 feet. Such inconsistency of course casts doubts on at least the earlier observations. Also the point on the island located by Sabine is uncertain; the earlier determinations used a lunar method not nearly as accurate as the modern one using broadcast time signals with sightings of the stars. Also the 1907 location was indirect, arrived at by triangulation from other locations. Yet the evidence does indicate that some westward drifting of Greenland is actually going on.

It is obvious, however, that the matter of present-day drifting is going to be settled only by precise astronomical determinations of latitude and longitude for at least a few well placed points scattered over the several continents, with those observations then repeated at sufficiently long intervals of time, say several decades apart. Needless to say, our modern methods, by which we map our world, are certainly precise enough. So we may properly expect, in a generation or so, to learn for sure whether the continents are now drifting, in what directions and how fast. So the final decision, as to present drifting at least, will be astronomical, "by the verdict of the stars," as the science historian Henry Smith Williams put it. On the other hand, if Joly is right, such drifting may now be very slight, this present being a period of relative substratum solidity and continental fixity. In other words, continental drifting may well be periodic, and this not the time for it.

Williams, in a popular book, *The Biography of Mother Earth* (1931), contributed two new ideas on the drifting of continents: first a somewhat different account of the paths of drifting, and second a new factor to explain such drifting.

### Paths of Drifting

Relying on the known geologic record, he tried to work out the paths of past drifting which would best explain what is known of changes of climates and travels of plants and animals in ages past. Wegener had begun with a single great continent, all the land then above sea level, which in due course split apart to form the several existing continents. Williams began by centering this single continental mass about the South Pole. Much of it was covered by an icecap, which by its weight and outward spreading probably helped in the breakup of the original land mass. First to break off from the continental margin was a wide wedge, shaped like the piece of pie every boy wants but never gets. It drifted slowly northward into warmer climatic zones and while under the equator bore the luxurious tropical vegetation which later became the belt of coal beds stretching from eastern Asia across North America into Europe. Notice that Williams puts Asia just west of North America, with Europe just east, those being their positions in this first wedge. Later they broke apart, the Asiatic portion then floating westward around the North Pole to meet Europe, finally jamming up the Ural Mountains of Russia between them.

According to Williams, India was not then a part of Asia, but was a small second wedge which later broke loose from the original south polar continent, moving northward and only recently crashing into Asia, piling up the young Himalayas as the crumpled wreckage. Finally a third and larger wedge came loose and drifted northward, breaking apart into South America, Africa, and Australia. Africa eventually jammed into Europe to fold and uplift the Alps, Pyrenees, Atlas, and other east-west ranges of southern Europe and northern Africa. Later separation then accounted for the Mediterranean Basin. Meanwhile the South American portion of the wedge drifted westward to make contact with North America in much the present manner. All this was of course intended to explain what we know of ancient distributions of land and sea, climates, plants, and animals. For as the continents drifted into new climatic zones, and conditions of life changed, old life forms were extinguished and new ones took their places. Migrations of land life occurred when the continents made contacts, and were interrupted when barriers of sea or mountains intervened.

Williams also offered a new explanation why the continents split apart and drifted. He began with that south polar continent back a billion or more years ago when life was just beginning. In due course that life evolved into those lowly forms which extract lime from the sea waters to make themselves protecting shells, then leave these shells as ever-deepening layers of limestone in all the shallows within and about the continents. By such adding to the protruding land mass, they eventually upset the flotational balance and forced readjustment by tidal pulls and centrifugal force driving those protruding continental masses toward the equator. However, this does not seem to account for the continued drifting toward the North Pole once the continental fragments had crossed the equator. At this point, Williams relied on a general northward shove as the original polar continent broke up and pushed outward. That initial breakup, however, was more likely due to the thickening and spreading of the great polar icecap, by its huge weight causing the Earth-crust to sink, thus forcing outward flowage of substratum matter carrying with it segments of continental crust.

### Two Polar Land Masses

Recently Dr. Fritz Kahn has offered still another version of the story of continental drifting in his book *The Design of the Universe* (1954). He concludes that the geologic facts indicate two early land masses, one about the South Pole, the other near the North Pole, with a roughly equatorial ocean between them. That ancient ocean has been long known to the geologists as Tethys, the southern land mass as Gondwana, and the northern one as Laurasia. According to Kahn, these two land masses move independently, each one pulled toward the equator largely by centrifugal force; "there they collide and then rebound," so that the sea between them narrows and widens. During the last quarter-billion years the northern mass has been more actively moving, during the previous quarter-billion years the southern mass. Recently, Africa has apparently crashed head-on against Asia and Europe, piling up mountains between them. But here and there the merged margins are coming apart, though not always just where they met. Thus Spain and Arabia belonged originally to the African land mass, but have been lost by attaching to Europe and Asia.

Our maps of today, over all the World, show many features suggesting continental drifting. Thus the advancing margins, such as the west coasts of the Americas, buckle up as they plow through the resisting substratum, upheaving coastal mountain ranges, such as our Rockies, Sierras, and Andes. Notice too how the southern tip of South America seems to drag behind, complete with remnant islands apparently torn off and left deserted in the Atlantic to the east. This is but one of a multitude of instances where the drag of the substratum on the "stern" of a drifting continent seems to break it up into islands left in its wake, as witness the marginal chains of the Aleutians, Kuriles, Japan, Philippines, East Indies, Madagascar, and our own West Indies.

So all in all, the evidence for continental drifting is growing, and being taken more and more seriously by geologists for explaining existing surface features, the climates of the past, and the distribution of plants and animals, both past and present.

## Shifting of the Whole Crust

Continental drifting, however, should not be confused with another seemingly related theory, that of general crustal shiftings of the entire Earth-crust *as a unified whole* over the surface of the globe. This is a rather old idea already broached before 1880 independently by Herder, Evans, and Wettstein, and later by a score of others, with variant emphases on the shifting of the crust itself, or of the poles and equator relative to the crust. The purpose was always to explain the past changes of climatic zones indicated by the geologic record.

The latest proponent of this theory is Charles H. Hapgood in his book *Earth's Shifting Crust* (1958). Unfortunately, though the author has been most industrious, as shown by his copious bibliography and numerous quotations, he is always the partisan advocate of his own pet theory and not at all the open-minded scientist following where the facts lead. Instead he has the unscientific habit of citing no facts or authorities clashing with his own conclusions, and of conveniently disposing of all conflicting theories by simply dismissing them. Thus his bibliography of 458 published items omits Williams' book and even Joly's *Surface History of the Earth*, both most pertinent. Joly and Wegener are referred to briefly, only to be summarily rejected without any statement of reasons. This of course renders his book of much less value. However, his ideas should still be considered on their own merits.

To explain the forces behind the wholesale crustal shifting, Hapgood calls in a collaborator, the engineer James H. Campbell. The co-authors hold that the cause is the accumulation of polar snows as heavy icecaps resting on land areas somewhat eccentric to the pole, itself not a new idea. Eventually

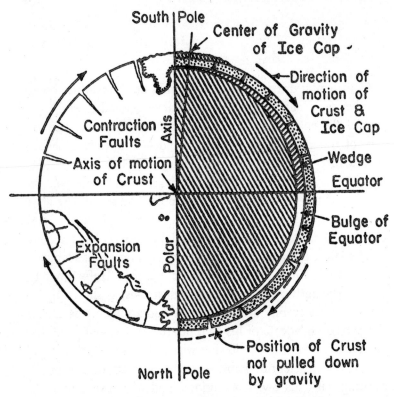

*Figure 17. Hapgood's Theory of Crustal Shifting*

(After James H. Campbell, in *Earth's Shifting Crust*, by C. H. Hapgood, Pantheon, 1958.)

such an increasingly heavy mass should weigh down and force the land deeper into the underlying substratum. But they contend that before this adjustment can occur, the centrifugal force of the Earth's rotation will drive the protruding excess mass toward the equator, carrying the whole Earth-crust with it as a single moving unit. As the icecap is thus moved into warmer zones, it naturally melts away, and the crustal shift stops, with the poles of the Earth now positioned over new points on the crust. Rather strangely, they do not call upon tidal pulls of the Moon and Sun, which would be very helpful partners in such equatorward shifting of the eccentric and uncompensated icecap masses.

The co-authors then point out that the new polar areas of the crust must now accumulate their own snow and ice. If these rest on solid land bottom, they too will build up heavy icecaps, and if eccentric to the poles, will in turn be drawn equatorward, to thrust the entire Earth-crust through another shift. In this way they explain our recent Ice Age as due to a North Pole over the Hudson Bay area, and as ending when that area moved southward from under the Pole. Before that, by repeated crustal shiftings, they place the Pole over Greenland, earlier over Alaska, and still earlier over north-central Siberia. And even before that, they suggest many previous shiftings of crust relative to poles, but find that the geologic evidence grows more vague as they go back in time, so that the earlier story just cannot be traced. However, it should be pointed out here that Wegener and others had already indicated these very same polar positions and related zonal climates, but produced by more local continental driftings rather than by general crustal shiftings.

At the present time, our co-authors point to the Antarctic icecap, its center of mass eccentric to the South Pole by three hundred or more miles along the 96th meridian east of Greenwich. As it grows in mass, it should start moving northward, and by shifting the whole Earth-crust, carry Siberia toward the North Pole, and North America away from it. Thus they try to explain not only the wanderings of polar glaciations, both North and South, but also all the other known alterations in past climates over the entire Earth.

### Objections to Crust Shifting

The basic weakness of the Hapgood-Campbell theory is undoubtedly the shifting of the *whole Earth-crust as a single unit*. It presupposes a strength and rigidity of the thin crust (comparable to a sheet of paper around an orange) sufficient to transmit a thrust practically around the World. Even a casual examination of the actual Earth-crust shows that it has no such strength and rigidity, but that instead any such local thrust has in fact always resulted only in nearby crumpling, folding, and faulting, without transmission to anywhere near the distances demanded by this theory. Obviously too, the power required to move the entire crust must be truly tremendous compared with that needed for producing merely local effects. Not only is the mass to be moved multiplied greatly by distance and extent, but the resistance likewise is multiplied. Before the thrust can possibly move the entire crust, it must be relieved by local crumpling.

Of course the crumplings and fissurings of the Earth-crust are too universal and manifest to be ignored, and the co-authors therefore try to explain them. If the Earth were not rotating, the force of gravity, working alone, would shape it into a practically perfect sphere. But it is in fact rotating daily, which introduces a centrifugal force causing distortion of the sphere into an oblate spheroid with an equatorial bulge. This bulge is slight, just 1/297, the equatorial radius being only 13.35 miles greater than the polar radius. Now if the crust shifts as a whole along any meridian, the portions approaching the equator must stretch and fissure to fit the increasing circumferences. Such fissures must then fill up with lavas which flow up from below and immediately solidify, thus making the crust permanently larger. Finally, having crossed the equator, the selfsame portions of crust thus enlarged will be moving poleward to smaller circumferences, being thereby subjected to compressions forcing folding and crumpling— and mountain-building.

Here Hapgood and Campbell claim to have made a great discovery, no less than the source of the mighty force that builds mountains. But unfortunately they base it upon a gross blunder. That is clearly a harsh statement which certainly must be fully sustained. Centrifugal force of rotation produces the equatorial bulge of the oblate Earth spheroid, represented most closely by the mean levels of the Earth's oceans. The resultant of the pull of gravity and this centrifugal force maintains the ocean surface in a continuous state of oblate spheroid balance, subject only to the passing disturbances of tides and waves. For us, sailing over this surface, it represents the *horizontal*, neither to be climbed uphill nor descended downhill. To start with, Hapgood and Campbell recognize this, and have that portion of the crust which approaches the equator moving horizontally, which it undoubtedly would, traveling neither uphill nor down. But once that portion of crust has crossed the equator, they forget this balanced horizontality of the surface and have their crustal moving *downhill* closer toward the Earth's center at the pole. In their own words, "The mountains are not lifted up at all; the surface is pulled down. . . . What pulled it down, obviously, was the force of gravity, and the reason it was pulled down was that it was first shifted horizontally to a place where gravity could act upon it . . . Here then, is the answer to the long-standing enigma of the source of energy for mountain building."

Actually and evidently it is no answer to any enigma whatever, for you cannot treat your surface movement as horizontal on one side of the equator and as downhill on the other side. Where our theorists have erred is to utilize centrifugal force on the approach side, and then wipe it out on the other side, in which convenient maneuver Nature unfortunately declines to co-operate. Were it truly possible, we would have Perpetual Motion at last; just slide a floating mass horizontally (not uphill) over the surface of the sea to the equator, then let it slide downhill to the pole (releasing potential energy on the way), again slide it horizontally back to the equator, and let it slide downhill again, ad infinitum.

It should also be pointed out that this theory of unit crustal shifting does not at all explain our primary problem posed by the close fit of the African and South American coasts, nor any other problem of apparent relative shifting of the continental masses. Also, virtually all the evidence adduced by Hapgood for unit crustal shifting is even more applicable to continental drifting. For one example, Hapgood cites as evidence for his own theory the recent work of the Chinese oceanographer Ting Ying Hi Ma on the growth of coral reefs as indicating past changes in positions of the equator, but Ting himself explains these changes by continental drifting.

### Causes of Continental Drifting

As our knowledge of the geologic record grows, the idea of continental drifting seems more and more necessary to interpret the accumulating facts. The impelling forces may be tidal, centrifugal, or both, acting on protruding and uncompensated masses such as icecaps or newly uplifted mountain ranges. Or such masses, slowly sinking to flotation balance, may force displacement and outward flowage of substratum matter, and be broken up and carried along on such flowage.

Another probable factor, so far strangely overlooked, is one that must result if the period of the Earth's rotation has in fact been gradually slowing up over the past billions of years, as seems generally agreed among astronomers and geodesists. For such lengthening of the day must have slowly reduced the centrifugal force, and therefore the resulting equatorial bulge of the Earth. The oblateness must have originally been something comparable to that of Jupiter (1/16) or Saturn (1/9), and then slowly decreased to its present 1/297. As it did so, the fluid oceans had to shift toward the poles, ever seeking the spheroid sea-level balance of the moment. The Earth-crust, however, being comparatively rigid and therefore less free to flow, would respond with a considerable lag, perhaps even intermittently, but yet would drift gradually poleward. It may well be that the flow of material would be largely in the more plastic substratum, but even that would tend to carry along the crustal surfaces floating upon it. Opposing such movement, however, would still be centrifugal force and the tidal pulls of Moon and Sun, both acting more effectively on any protruding or isostatically uncompensated continental masses, thereby causing variations, perhaps even temporary retreats, in their driftings.

The known geologic record clearly shows periodic submergences and depositions in shallow seas, alternating with mountain-folding and uplift, and this suggests some cyclic mechanism, driven probably by radioactive heat, equivalent in effect to that of Joly. This probably means periods of easier and more rapid drifting, alternating with periods of relative crustal fixity. As we progress in working out the correlations of cyclic stages, past datings, and paths of drifting, we will probably find that certain major movements prevail, such as a general westward tidal drift, but this coupled with many local irregularities. Thus uneven melting (or solidifying) of substratum, or the varying thicknesses within each continental mass, would mean that some points would remain or become anchored, to serve as pivots of rotation. Even irregularities in shape and extent could cause differences in speeds and directions, introducing clashes and rotational swirls. So the patterns of drifts and turns would be chaotic and difficult to decipher and follow, rather than simple and easily traceable. But the major movements may yet be some day worked out in accord with indications of changing climatic conditions and of migrations of ancient plants and animals, and thus give us at least rough drift maps of our World at the several crucial stages of its billion-year history.

Indeed, such a reconstruction of the past seems to be promised by the new science of paleomagnetism. It rests upon the fact that when rocks of magnetic composition are laid down, either as sediments or lavas, they take on a magnetic polarity which they thereafter retain. If then they are later shifted in direction—as by continental drifting—that fact is revealed by the misdirected alignment of what we may call their "fossil magnetism." What is important here is the fact that the recent paleomagnetic surveys of the continents do broadly indicate that Europe and North America, and Africa and South America, have been drifting apart during the last two hundred million years, and that India has drifted from south to north across the equator during the last seventy million years. Furthermore, Australia has apparently drifted along a rather devious but traceable course around the south pole during the past billion years.

However, such magnetic evidence, though it is suggestive, must not be taken as really conclusive. For one thing, even now the north and south magnetic poles do not correspond in positions with the poles of Earth rotation, and in fact are not exactly opposite each other on the globe. We know too that the whole magnetic map of the World has shifted appreciably in the last few hundred years. Also the fossil magnetism itself indicates repeated complete reversals of polarity in the Earth's magnetism. In fact, we do not even know what conditions or structures cause that magnetism, nor what makes it shift or reverse. And until we learn much more, we cannot be certain that these indications really mean continental drifting, instead of some quite unrelated wandering and reversals of the magnetic poles.

More significant evidence of continental drifting, however, has just been published by a research team at the Lamont Geological Laboratory of Columbia University, consisting of David B. Ericson, Maurice Ewing, Goesta Wollin, and Bruce G. Heezen. After a study of 221 cores taken from the Atlantic and Caribbean ocean bottoms, they conclude that these ocean basins as we know them came into existence during the Cretaceous Period, for none of the core contents proved older than one hundred million years. This is wholly consistent with a breaking and drifting apart of the Eastern and Western continents to form the Atlantic Basin between them.

CHAPTER **10**

## CLIMATES DO CHANGE

Our weather, of course, is constantly changing from day to day and season to season. But does climate, which seems so stable within historic times, also change over the ages recorded by geology?

The answer of the geologist is quite definite: climates do indeed change with time. When he finds deep beds of coal containing fossils of tropical swamp plants, beds which now form a great belt stretching from Pennsylvania through New England, Nova Scotia, the British Isles, and Central Europe and on to southern Russia, he knows that the climate of that now temperate belt must have been that of an equatorial jungle a quarter of a billion years ago during the Carboniferous Period. In the same way, plant fossils found in Arctic Spitzbergen and in icebound Antarctica tell of at least temperate climates in times past where freezing temperatures now prevail. Does this mean that the Earth as a whole has been getting cooler? Not at all, for the geologist also finds in now tropic lands the unmistakable signs of ancient ice action and glaciation. On the whole the evidence indicates that the overall temperatures of Sun and Earth have not seriously altered during geologic times, though local climates over the Earth have certainly changed.

The word *climate* comes from the Greek *klino* which means *slope*. It embodies the ancient Greek belief that the flat world sloped upward toward the North, downward toward the South, and that northern cold and southern warmth were really due to this difference in elevations.

## Our Zonal Climates

Today we know better, that the Earth is a rotating globe heated by the rays of the Sun, and understand that our climates are basically zonal, with high tropic temperatures under the intense vertical rays at the equator, low frigid temperatures under the slanting and spread-out rays at the poles, with intermediate temperatures in the zones between.

But because the axis of the Earth's rotation is inclined toward the plane of its yearly revolution about the Sun, there is an alternate tipping of the two poles toward and from the Sun, producing the annual cycle of seasonal changes in zonal temperatures through summer, autumn, winter, and spring.

Also the differential heating of the atmosphere causes a general zonal pattern of air circulation by surface winds northward and southward, with return winds at higher levels in opposite directions. These, however, are displaced by the rotation of the Earth so that they do not move due north or south, but angle eastward or westward. And even these wind zones vary seasonally, shifting poleward in the summers and equatorward in the winters.

As part of such zonal circulation, there are also over-all vertical eddies with zones of rising and sinking air currents. Rising currents cause air expansion and cooling, and the condensing of moisture as rain or snow. On the other hand, sinking currents cause warming and drying, resulting in two

belts of arid deserts circling the Earth roughly a third of the
way from the equator toward the poles.

Prevailing surface wind directions cause ocean currents by
friction between the moving air and the surface waters of
the seas. There are then return currents elsewhere at the surface or in the ocean depths, producing a slow general circulation of ocean waters, and of their heat and salinity. Such ocean
currents, carrying heat or cold, greatly modify the climates of
adjacent land areas, but on the whole tend to equalize their
temperatures.

While these are some of the basic factors determining zonal
climates, there are many local variations due largely to the
varying shapes and relations between lands and seas, and their
respective elevations and depths. Very marked among such
local effects are those produced by mountain ranges across
the paths of warm moist winds. As the air is shoved up on
the windward slope of the mountains, it expands, cools, and
precipitates its load of moisture as rain or snow. Then, emptied
of moisture, it slides down the leeward slope, becomes dense,
warm, and dry, drinking up all moisture thirstily, drying interior valleys and plains to a desert aridity. Such, for example,
are the chinook winds of our interior West, which after such
drying, sweep down upon foothills, valleys, and plains, and
often overnight melt and evaporate away even deep snowdrifts
that it took a whole winter to accumulate.


## Climatic Revolutions


We have already noted in Chapter 8 the historic fact of
cyclic geologic Revolutions, marked by the uplift of great
mountain ranges, usually in formerly depressed areas submerged under shallow transgressing seas in which sedimentary

strata had been deposited. Now we realize that such mountain uplifts must have also caused serious revolutions in climates, serious at least to the plant and animal life struggling to survive. The very uplift caused lower temperatures, as every snow-capped mountain peak now testifies, while the raising of the mountain barrier would cut off moisture-bearing winds and so cause aridity to leeward. Thus the geologically recent uplift of the Himalayas cut off the warm moist winds from the Indian Ocean and turned the interior of Asia into the barren Gobi Desert. Such too was the effect of the geologically recent uplift of our North American West Coast mountains, producing the relatively dry interior, ranging from grassy plains to arid deserts.

Mountain-building is normally part of a general lesser uplift of continental proportions, less spectacular perhaps, but still far-reaching in its geologic and climatic effects. For example, back about a hundred million years ago in the Cretaceous Period, the North American interior (roughly the whole present basin of the Mississippi and its tributaries) was inundated by a shallow sea extending northward from our Gulf of Mexico. But then began a slow uplift of the continent, causing the shores of the transgressing sea to retire southward. As they did so, the sandy beaches were replaced by marginal swamps full of characteristic plant and animal life. With further uplift, forests took the place of swamps, and eventually these gave way, first in patches, finally over wide areas, to grassy plains. Meanwhile the forms of life changed, even the animal life. One notable example, for which we have an ample fossil record, is the adaptive evolution of the horses to fit the changing conditions. The earliest horse we know was Eohippus, meaning "dawn-horse," no larger than a big cat, who wandered over forested bottom-lands on wide, many-toed feet, browsing with soft teeth on tender leaves, and readily concealable because of a mottled or striped coat which blended into the background. But as the land rose and grassy plains displaced the woodland, he grew in stature, developing long legs with lighter one-toed (hoofed) feet for swift running on hard ground, both for better escape from hungry enemies and for wide grazing. That grazing on harsh grasses then developed hard cutting and grinding teeth and a long neck and head to reach down to graze despite the long legs.

However, the causes of climatic changes are not always so clear. Thus one great known change was so recent in geologic time and so far-reaching in its effects that we will do well to cover it in detail. Besides, it is one of the scientific mysteries which have not been fully unraveled to this day.

### Mystery of Erratic Boulders

It began with a problem which proved completely baffling to the scientific world of the early nineteenth century. Scattered over northern Europe and North America were innumerable boulders of varying sizes which were plainly out of place. They were not like the bedrock belonging to the neighborhood, and were therefore called *erratics*. In fact, the nearest bedrock like them was often hundreds of miles away. Something must have moved them all these long distances, but no one seemed to know just what. Except the Irish peasants—they knew. At least they firmly contended that the many and often huge erratics of Ireland had been brought by the old-time Viking invaders as ballast for their ships. However, that legendary explanation was just as good as the best that the scientists then offered.

Many of the scientific authorities simply gave it up. Wind and water certainly could not have transported boulders which often weighed tens of tons. So utterly baffled were they in fact, that Charles Darwin tells of a Mr. Cotton he met, "who knew a good deal about rocks," of whom he remarks, "he solemnly assured me that the world will come to an end before any one would be able to explain how this stone came where it lay," referring of course to one of these huge erratics.

Many geologists of that day, in this as in other matters, turned for explanation to Noah's Flood. They assumed that somehow swift currents set in, lifting and carrying these massive boulders as if they were corks. Just in itself that seemed hard to believe, but became impossible when the positions of some erratics were considered. For in the valleys of the Alps and Jura Mountains such boulders were often poised high on the steep slopes, and in such precarious balance that any swift rush of floodwaters could not have left them there, but would have tumbled them rolling down the valley sides. Of course, an occasional accident might have happened, but there were thousands of them thus unstably placed.

That same precarious perching of the erratics on the hillside slopes helped explode another theory, offered by the German geologist Leopold von Buch, who thought that nearby mountain ranges had suddenly sprung up, catapulting these rocks to great distances. But how could erratics, falling thus in violent bombardment, have possibly alighted so gently as not to roll down into the valleys? Besides which we now know that mountain ranges do not pop up suddenly that way, but take simply ages to uprear their vast bulks.

Finally in 1830 a scientific explanation did come from the great English geologist Sir Charles Lyell. He held that the regions where we now find erratics had at one time been submerged beneath the sea, and that icebergs, floating down from glaciers in the North, would carry much rock rubbish, including just such boulders as these. When the icebergs melted, their load of rocks was dropped in these strange positions, presumably sinking gently through the buoyant waters to their present places on what was then sea bottom. For a time this theory found wide favor, not as completely satisfactory, but as least objectionable. It is now held true, however, in only the few cases where the land is known to have been actually submerged below sea level so that icebergs could have carried erratics to their present places.

### Discovering the Ice Age

Meanwhile, however, a more satisfactory solution was offered by a man who made no claim to being a scientist and who certainly had no notion how widely his solution was to be applied. He was just a Swiss mountaineer, Perraudin by name, an observing chamois hunter of the Alps. Quite unaware of the elaborate and ingenious theories concocted by scientific men, he drew some simple conclusions from what he saw before his own eyes. He was thoroughly familiar with glaciers, those winding rivers of ice which crept slowly down his mountain valleys, bearing on their backs much rock waste in which were mixed many boulders like those mysterious erratics of the hillsides. He understood how the moving ice plucked these rocks off the mountainsides and bore them far down into the valleys, finally dropping them there at the glacier fronts as the ice melted in the warmth of the lowlands. His simple explanation for these puzzling erratics, poised high up on the valley slopes and far beyond the glaciers themselves, was merely that the glaciers had once been larger, mounting higher upon the slopes and stretching farther down into the valleys. In short, the erratics had been carried and placed by larger old-time glaciers now shrunken or even melted away.

Perraudin broached his idea in the year 1815, and was merely laughed at. But eight years later his civil-engineer friend M. Venetz wrote a paper on it, and this came to the attention of the geologist Jean de Charpentier, who soon became an enthusiastic supporter of the theory. However, he did little with it for thirteen years, but finally, in 1836, presented the idea to Louis Agassiz, the Swiss naturalist. Though at first skeptical, Agassiz was soon convinced and then started a most thoroughgoing study of glaciers, erratics, and everything else bearing on ice action. This study included all erratics wherever found, not just in obvious glacier valleys of mountains like the Alps and Juras, but elsewhere through the world, over quite flat country as well. He soon came to a startling conclusion: that not so long ago, as the geologist talks of time, northern Europe, practically all of Canada, and a large part of the northern United States had been covered with vast thick sheets of glacial ice. He held that these great ice sheets moved southward, bearing on and within them those erratic boulders we now find widely scattered where the melting ice finally dumped them. "Thus," said the science historian Henry Smith Williams, "the commonplace induction of the chamois hunter blossomed in the mind of Agassiz into the conception of a universal ice age."

The idea made a profound impression on the scientific world: the problem of erratics had at last been solved. Of course, there was ridicule in some quarters, frank scepticism in others. But when Sir Charles Lyell and William Buckland, the leading geologists of the day, gave their support, the theory quickly gained general acceptance which has been wholly justified by the mass of evidence since brought to light.

For glaciers and ice sheets work in their own distinctive ways and leave very characteristic and easily recognized marks. No other agency but glacial ice, be it on land or afloat at sea, bears

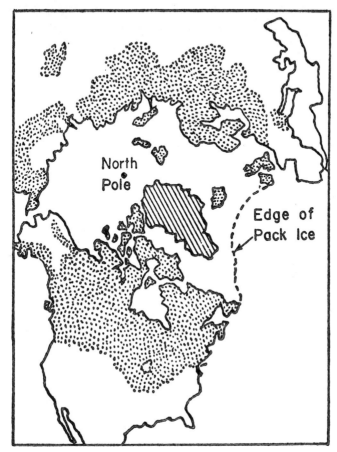

*Figure 18. Extent of Pleistocene Ice Sheets*

Dotted—Maximum extent of ice sheets. Lined—Present Greenland ice sheet. (Taken from the Glacial Map of North America, Richard Foster Flint, Chairman, The Geological Society of America Special Paper Co.)

erratics to such out-of-place places. No other agency but moving glacial ice scratches and gouges the bedrock over which it drags, so that anyone can read not only the fact that the ice had come that way, but the very direction in which it moved. Sometimes the overriding ice planed down or rounded off the protruding ledges of bedrock into very characteristic forms, which again reveal the direction of movement, the lee side being usually plucked by the ice freezing onto and dragging away part of the rock mass, thus providing the erratics which were then to be left somewhere farther along. Obviously too, the boulders themselves tell the direction of the ice movement, for if one traces them to the bedrock from which they were thus plucked, we know they came from that way. So we know, for instance, that the ice sheet which covered Manhattan Island moved in from the northwest across the Hudson River because many of the erratics of Manhattan, Brooklyn, and Long Island came from the Palisades along the west bank of the Hudson.

So there was soon no question about the truth of the Ice Age theory. And that meant that regions now blooming with summer vegetation must have been completely covered all year round with a deep moving sheet of glacial ice. Somewhere snow had piled up year after year, never melting all away, but packing more and more compactly into blue glacier ice. As it piled up in the centers of snow accumulation, the surface sloped more and more outward toward the edges of the ice sheet. That caused the whole mass to flow outward under the force of gravitation. Being quite solid, the icy mass could press on over and around obstacles such as hills and even mountains. But if solid, how could the ice flow at all? We are not so sure just how, though we do know that it does in every mountain glacier and in the present great ice sheets of Greenland and Antarctica. The usual theory is that the ice melts slightly under pressure, moves a bit to relieve the pressure, and then refreezes. That way the whole mass can slowly creep forward. An odd fact is that the ice can actually move uphill, if only the surface of the ice slopes in the direction of the motion. You can see how by pouring cold molasses on the center of a dish. As it heaps up, it flows outward and even uphill over the edge of the dish.

### Extent of the Ice Sheets

We now know that the ice sheets once covered about a million and a quarter square miles of northern Europe and about four million in North America. Our American ice sheets had their centers of snow accumulation up in Canada, one out in the western mountains, a second just west of Hudson Bay, another just east of the Bay, and perhaps a fourth in Newfoundland. The present ice sheet of Greenland seems to be a fifth center not yet uncovered, or perhaps accumulated later than the others. Naturally the ice spread out in all directions, but most of it went south. That way the ice was continually melting in the warmer climate, giving place for more ice pressed out from the center. The limit of its extension would be reached where the melting just equaled and balanced the outward movement. At that limit the ice turned to water which flowed off by whatever channels it could find, bearing with it the finely ground silt that makes glacial streams so milky. It would also wash much of the sand and gravel out into a flat plain bordering the limit of the ice sheet, the so-called *outwash plain*. But the boulders, rocks, pebbles, and even coarse gravels would be dumped unsorted just where the ice happened to melt, leaving a *moraine* of mixed material called *drift* or *till* which the veriest amateur in geology can always recognize. Those dump heaps of the ice sheet are most irregular, a rounded hill here, a kettle hole there, no order anywhere, just one gravelly, pebbly, bouldery mess.

In our Eastern states, the southern limit of the ice invasion is distinctly marked by a clear terminal moraine. Farther west it is no longer a clear moraine, but just a scattering of erratic boulders and other ice signs. That limit extends the length of Long Island as its backbone of rounded gravel hills, while to the south stretch the level outwash plains of sand. The border line then crosses Staten Island and winds across northern New Jersey, proceeds northwestward through the mountains of Pennsylvania, and turns southwest near Buffalo toward Cincinnati. After following the Ohio River for a ways, it loops northward toward Indianapolis, thence southwest to St. Louis, and follows the Missouri Valley to the east line of Montana. From there it proceeds westward with a lot of minor irregularities to the Pacific Coast. To the north of that line, nearly the whole continent was covered with great creeping ice sheets, sometimes miles thick. Strangely enough, northeastern Alaska remained free of ice, as did also a "glacial island" in southwestern Wisconsin (with an overlap into Minnesota, Iowa, and Illinois). In these unglaciated areas we find no erratics or moraines, but only the unaltered bedrock such as we find south of the ice-sheet limit. But nearly everywhere north of that line, one can read the signs of the Great Ice Age in every rolling hill and dug-out sandbank. This includes our most populated states, and here just anyone whose eyes have been opened can read of the wonders underfoot, the thrilling tale of how the mile-thick ice mass plowed down from the frigid north, again and again reshaping our landscapes to what they are today.

### Glacial Aftereffects

For heavy moving ice sheets worked just like a haphazard bulldozer, shoving surface earth before it, even carrying earth within it, and then in the end, dumping everything carelessly. Here it would level and scour, elsewhere pile up dumps which it would not trouble to level off flat, leaving hills and holes, the latter filling in with ponds and lakes, some unconnected, others oddly joined by rambling stream courses. Old stream beds would often be filled in, and new ones would have to be found. As a result, a haphazard drainage system is a pretty sure sign the ice sheets were once there.

Another odd feature of the Ice Age left its interesting story recorded here and there. When the ice sheet was at its very thickest and heaviest, its sheer weight pressed down the earth-crust below it, more of course toward the heavier center, less so at the thinner margins. Then when the ice melted away, and the load lightened, the earth-crust heaved upward in re-lief, up toward its normal levels of isostatic balance. Mean-while the edge of the ice was receding. Not that the ice actu-ally moved backward toward the north, but merely that it melted away faster than it moved forward. Then between the receding ice front and any embankments to the south (usually moraines left by the ice itself) there formed bodies of water, ranging from mere puddles and ponds to great, but temporary, lakes. The greatest of these was glacial Lake Agassiz, extending northward some seven hundred miles from Minnesota into Canada. Many such temporary lakes of course formed along the ice front, several in the New York area being named after present localities, as Lakes Flushing, Hudson, Hackensack, and Passaic. In this same area, by the sinking of the earth-crust toward the north, the entire length of the Hudson-Champlain Valley was inundated by the sea right up to the St. Lawrence, making New England a temporary island. Proof of this are the fossils of whales, walruses, and lesser sea animals found along the full length of this inlet. These fossils are now found some seventy feet above sea level at Manhattan Island,

400 feet above at the south end of Lake Champlain, and
500 feet above at the lake's north end, all these elevations
representing the local uplifts of the crust since the load of
glacial ice was removed. Further evidence of such uplift is
furnished by the old beaches, found not only along the Hudson-Champlain Inlet, but notably along the old shores of Lake
Agassiz and other ice-front lakes. These beaches invariably
slope upward toward the north. They were of course originally
laid down level along the shores of the times, but have since
been upraised as the earth-crust upheaved, more toward the
north.

Notable among the remarkable postglacial stories is that of
the Great Lakes and Niagara Falls, and the gorge the falls
cut in receding upstream. In general, the ice sheets at their
maxima quite filled the basins of the Great Lakes and helped
to gouge them out somewhat deeper. The ice thereby blocked
all the present drainage outlets and forced the waters from the
melting front to drain to the south, much of it by way of the
Mississippi and its tributaries. But as the ice front receded
northward, lakes formed in the southern ends of the basins,
and step by step found eastward outlets in front of the ice, the
more southerly outlets being uncovered first, the more north-
erly ones later. The Niagara connection between Lakes Erie
and Ontario had, as a result, a most varied history. An old
channel was filled with glacial rubbish, so a new one had to be
found, its course the present lower gorge below the Great
Whirlpool. At one time only Lake Erie drained through it, so
the stream was small, cutting only a narrow gorge and that
very slowly. Later the other Upper Great Lakes, one after the
other, added to its stream, much multiplied by rapid melting
from the ice front. But then the Niagara channel was again
largely abandoned by the opening of more northerly outlets.

Finally, however, the earth-crust rose and cut off these north-erly outlets, and once more Niagara became the main outlet stream. All this story, far more complicated than is here re-counted, is now reflected in the varying widths and depths of the Niagara gorge as thus cut by the varying flows and falls of the water.

### Retreat of the Ice Front

Now all this is obviously fairly recent geologic history, and we naturally ask just when it happened, a question to which the glacial geologists have paid much attention. Thus it was hoped, by measuring how fast the falls are now receding up the Niagara gorge, to estimate the total time for cutting the full length of the gorge. That figure was first given as about seven thousand years, but it soon became evident that the rate of recession had greatly varied because of the many changes in the Great Lakes, so that estimate was not relied upon. How-ever, the same method applied to the recession of St. Anthony Falls up the Mississippi gorge at Minneapolis gave a more reliable estimate of nearly eight thousand years since the ice sheet left that locality, which was in fair agreement with the Niagara results.

But already a more dependable method had been proposed as early as 1832 by the American geologist Alfred Smith, and in 1884 applied by a Swede, Baron Gerard de Geer, to work out a year-by-year calendar of the recession of the European ice front in the area of the Baltic Sea, from northern Germany up through Denmark, Finland, and Sweden. It consisted in counting the number of layers of clay deposits laid down along the edge of the melting ice front, each layer representing a year, much as we measure the age of a tree by counting annual growth rings.

We have noted that as the ice front melted back, ponds and lakes formed here and there, banked on the south by ridges of the earth surface, and on the north by the ice itself. The waters of melting would be muddy with silts and gravels carried in and upon the advancing ice. During the summers, when melting was rapid, the swiftly flowing waters would carry the finer silts down the drainage streams, but would let the coarse gravels settle at once to the pond or lake bottoms. On the other hand, when the cold of winter stopped all melting, the flow of water slackened, permitting the fine silts to settle slowly in the still waters to form a denser layer of smeary clay. Each passing year was thus marked by an alternating pair of gravel and clay layers, each pair being called a *varve*, the Swedish word for *cycle*.

Fortunately, the layers differed from year to year. Unusually hot or long summers produced thicker gravel layers, or differing soil material caused deposits of distinctive colors or kinds. Such varying layers can often be identified over wide areas in a number of clay pits, and it becomes possible to compare and overlap such local records so as to get a fairly continuous series extending over thousands of years. In northern Sweden, Baron de Geer was thus able to trace a complete series right up to the very fronts of existing snow fields where just such layers of clay are still being laid down, thus connecting his entire calendar of glacial recession with current dates. The entire record, though it does not go back to the very beginning of the European ice retreat, does take us back to the year 11,800 B.C.

After the year 1900, several American geologists got busy, digging into clay pits along the Passaic, Hackensack, Hudson, Connecticut, and Merrimac Rivers, making detailed records

*Figure 19.   Recession of the European Ice Front*

(By permission from *The Last Glaciation*, by Ernst Antevs, American Geographical Society.)

of their glacial *varves*, which they then carefully placed to-gether into a continuous record on which some 4300 years could be counted. Then, in the 1920s, Ernst Antevs, a former associate of Baron de Geer, was making his way into the wilds of Canada, laboriously gathering data on clay layers in an effort to extend the series and fix definite dates for all the various stages of ice melting and recession. He did add a long series of some 1500 years between the Great Lakes and Hudson Bay, but could not connect them with the New England and New York series because there was a great gap between in Nature's record. And he found no way of connecting his series with current dates, though he did attempt by other means to correlate the recessions in Europe and North America with each other, though with much uncertainty. Only recently, by the very different Carbon-14 method, have we been able to fill in such gaps and fix past dates with fair certainty, but we will put that off to the final chapter when we will consider all the important modern methods for geologic dating.

### Earlier Glacial Periods

Of course, scientists want to know why the glacial ice sheets formed and then receded, and many scientific men (and even more unscientific ones) have tackled that problem. But before we too tackle it, we must face one important fact: it has happened again and again. Thus the geologic record shows unmistakable signs of widespread glaciation about a billion years ago in the Proterozoic Era, about half that long ago in the Paleozoic Period, a quarter-billion years ago in the Permian Period, and finally in the recent Pleistocene. Moreover, at least that last and best recorded glaciation was itself not continuous, but consisted of four great advances of the ice sheets, with warm interglacial periods in between. The first or Günz invasion occurred about 600,000 years ago. The Mindel glaciation came next, about 450,000 years ago; the third or Riss glaciation was about 250,000 years ago. The most recent or Würm glaciation ended roughly 11,000 years ago, but consisted of several minor advances and recessions, all of which have been worked out in considerable detail from local superim-

*Plate XVII.* CRAB NEBULA IN TAURUS. M 1. NGC 1952. Expanding nebulous remains of exploding supernova of A.D. 1054 observed by Chinese. The gaseous commotion causes strong radio emission. (Mount Wilson and Palomar Observatories.)

*Plate* XVIII. Moon at First Quarter. See Figure 12 for Key Map to features mentioned in the text. (Lick Observatory.)

Plate XIX. Moon at Last Quarter. See Figure 12 for Key Map to features mentioned the text. (Lick Observatory.)

*Plate XX.* THE FULL MOON. Shows white ray system of crater Tycho. (Lick Observatory.

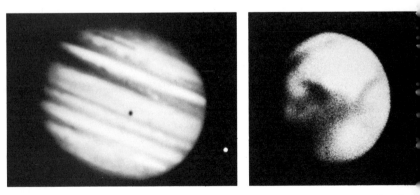

[LEFT] *Plate XXI.* JUPITER AND A SATELLITE. Photo shows planet belts, one of its larg satellites and its shadow on planet's surface. [RIGHT] *Plate XXII.* PLANET MARS. Phot by red light shows Mars in phase, dark and light areas and southern polar cap. (Moun Wilson and Palomar Observatories.)

positions of various kinds of glacial drift, etc. We are now apparently living in a warm interglacial period, perhaps to be followed by another advance of the northern ice sheets.

## Causes of Ice Ages

Obviously any proper explanation of the Ice Ages must tell us not only why they come and go, but also why they thus repeat by advancing and retreating within each general period. And that is by no means a simple problem. We have already noted the several explanations based on drifting of continents, shifting of earth-crust, or wandering of the axis and poles of Earth-rotation. These simply place each area being glaciated under and about the position of a pole of the moment, with the changes due to either the pole or the land areas shifting their positions. Much of this has already been discussed in Chapter 9.

There are also a number of theories that suffer from the fact that they cannot be checked against any past record of assumed causes. Such, for example, are the ideas that glacial periods are due to variations in radiation by the Sun, or due to a changing amount of carbon dioxide in the atmosphere, or passage of the solar system through a dust cloud in space, etc. None of these explanations are intrinsically impossible, but how can we now check up on such irregular, accidental, and unrecorded events of the remote past?

There are, however, a series of slow astronomical cycles which we do know are going on steadily, in the past, present, and future, and these, in suitable combinations, may also cause recurring glaciations. In the 1920s the Yugoslav geophysicist Milutin Milankovic drew up a time chart of these cycles which seems to explain both the occurrence and timing of recent glaciations, and even forecasts a bit into the future.

First it must be explained that the decisive factor in producing growing ice sheets seems to be shorter and cooler summers with reduced melting of the accumulated winter snows. Longer and colder winters apparently are less important—variations in temperature above freezing affect melting, while temperature variations below freezing hardly matter at all. So the problem for Milankovic was to locate those combinations of astronomical positions which caused short cool summers, particularly in the Northern Hemisphere.

The astronomical changes themselves are well known to be due to gravitational pulls between the Earth, the Moon, and the planets, particularly the overwhelmingly massive Jupiter. There are first slow changes in the elliptical orbit of the Earth: (1) a waxing and waning in its eccentricity, and (2) a swing of the axis of eccentricity around the Sun, in periods varying from 60,000 to 120,000 years. To this add certain shiftings of the Earth's axis of rotation caused by the pull of the Moon on the Earth's equatorial bulge, causing (3) changes in the angle of tilt of the axis, and (4) a precession of the axis in a period of about 26,000 years. When these cycles combine to produce an age of short cool summers in the Northern Hemisphere, growth in northern ice sheets may be expected, and the chart Figure 21 shows a remarkable coincidence between the dates thus calculated and the actual glacial invasions as dated by the geologists.

Furthermore we can project this astronomical chart into the future to predict that the Northern Hemisphere will get warmer until about 20,000 A.D., followed by cooling and ice invasions at about 50,000 A.D. and 90,000 A.D., though these glacial invasions should be less severe than those of the Great Ice Age of the geologically recent past.

## Arctic Seesaw Theory

There is still another theory of the cause of the Ice Age which has recently found favor among many scientific men. It was offered by geophysicist Maurice Ewing, director, and William Donn, meteorologist, of Columbia University's Lamont Geological Laboratory. They had learned from deep-sea sediments taken from the ocean bottoms of the Atlantic, Caribbean, and Gulf of Mexico, that the ocean had rather suddenly changed from cold to warm about 11,000 years ago. Wondering why, they hit upon this theory:

The Arctic Ocean is now almost enclosed by land, the main opening to the Atlantic being between Norway and Greenland. But across that opening extends an undersea ridge often less than three hundred feet below the surface, which rather effectively blocks currents interchanging the waters between the two oceans. The Arctic is now cold and largely frozen over. But if in the past the general sea level had been higher so that this channel was deeper, the ocean waters would have exchanged more freely. The Atlantic Ocean would then have been colder than now, and the Arctic Ocean warmer. Evaporation from the Arctic would then have been greater and the precipitation of snow over neighboring Greenland, Canada, and northern Europe greater, causing the accumulation of the ice sheets of the glacial period.

But the locking up of so much water in the ice sheets would have eventually lowered the general sea level by several hundred feet, which would again cut off the Arctic-Atlantic interchange of waters, and so end the warm Arctic Ocean and its piling up of nearby snow fields and ice sheets. Thus a seesaw cycle of ice ages and interglacial periods would result. Obviously, however, this does not explain why there were no ice ages for millions of years prior to the Pleistocene series, but for that Ewing and Donn turn to the theory of wandering poles already discussed.

Tending to confirm this Arctic seesaw theory, they found that ocean-bottom sediments from the Arctic Ocean show minute animal life indicating warm waters that ended about 11,000 years ago. Furthermore, they gathered the reports of anthropologists agreeing that human beings had occupied the shores of the Arctic Ocean until about that time, indicating its greater warmth.

A rather important inference from this theory must be noted. Careful world-wide measurements indicate that the level of the sea is now slowly rising and that the Arctic Ocean ice floe is rather rapidly melting. If this goes on, there will be freer exchanges of water between the Arctic and Atlantic and the return of the conditions starting a glacial period. This is of course in direct opposition to the forecast based on the astronomical cycles, and may therefore serve as a test (unfortunately some thousands of years hence) between the two theories. But by the time we can thus decide between these several theories, we may find that actually all these factors play parts in determining the coming and going of ice sheets.

### Related Aftereffects

Returning now to the certainties, we do know there have been ice ages, geologically recent, and recurring again and again. And we can note aftereffects not only in the areas actually invaded by the ice sheets themselves, but all about their borders, and even in remoter areas as well. These are largely due to two results of the melting away of the ice sheets.

First the levels of the world's oceans must have been lowered by several hundred feet by removal of the waters locked up in the great mass of the miles-thick ice sheets. With the melting of the ice, the sea level was slowly rising. Second, the earth-crust had sunk under the enormous weight of the ice masses, and now with melting the ice sheets thinned and the ice front gradually retreated toward the north. Thereupon the crust upheaved, first to the south, then progressively northward, with ever changing tilting.

In the Baltic area, wholly covered by the ice sheet at its maximum, the result was an involved series of inland freshwater lakes and of bays of the ocean connected in turn with the White Sea and the North Sea, a history we can now reconstruct from the distribution of various shells left along the shifting shore lines. The changes were of course due to the nip-and-tuck race between the rising level of the ocean and the uplift (and tilting) of the earth-crust, with sometimes the one ahead, sometimes the other.

A much simpler, yet far more important effect occurred in the basin of the Mediterranean. The ice sheets never got that far south, but at their maximum they lowered the ocean level below the connecting channel at Gibraltar. Because the waters of the Mediterranean evaporate faster than they are replenished by rain and inflowing rivers, the water-level within the basin is now continuously maintained by inflow from the Atlantic. But with this supply cut off, the water-level within the basin was lowered until there were only two big inland lakes separated by the barrier of Italy and Sicily. As neither had any outward drainage other than one into the other, they were probably salty, but the eastern one less so because of greater dilution by the inflow of several great rivers, the Nile of course, and by two great rivers from the north which we may name the Adriatic and the Aegean. The eastern lake, because it was thus better fed by inflow, was probably higher in level, and may have overflowed into the western lake, in which case it was probably fresh, and the western lake that much saltier.

At this time, as we know from both their fossil remains and the handmade tools they left, various races of primitive man inhabited this part of the world and undoubtedly occupied this mild and fruitful valley down to the very shores of these great lakes. But some ten thousand years ago (perhaps even less), the rising Atlantic waters reached the bottom of the Gibraltar channel and began flowing over into the inland basin. The result was catastrophic, for the stream quickly cut its bed deeper, even producing a long trench extending well out to the west across the Atlantic shelf, until it poured in an enormous flood which slowly refilled the interior valley, first the basin to the west, but eventually that to the east also. All this meant an inundation of the homes, fields, pastures, and hunting grounds of the primitive dwellers of the great valley, driving them to outward migrations and inevitably into conflict with neighboring peoples and often to extermination of one or the other.

Perhaps connected in some way with the Mediterranean refilling, though we do not really understand how, there came on a great change of climate to the south, probably about 5000 to 4000 B.C. First discovered half a century ago by French desert patrols, it was not really studied until a few years ago and then finally reported on in 1958 by the French ethnologist-explorer Henri Lhote. Before that change the very center of the Sahara was well watered by rivers, now become only dry beds, and was inhabited by an abundant human population which left its color paintings on the walls of cliffs depicting both themselves and the animals they hunted. They were apparently driven out finally by increasing aridity, westward perhaps as the primitive Egyptians, and southward into Central

Africa, if we may go by the cultures they show in these ancient wall paintings.

Aside from the complete reshaping of our northern landscapes, a most important result of the great ice invasions of the Pleistocene must be mentioned if only in passing. The climatic changes must have been many, and drastic and far-reaching, involving a multitude of severe hardships on all life forms. And the fossil record tells plainly that it was in this very period that Mankind first appeared, evolved, and made his ancient basic progress. Among the anthropologists there is rather universal agreement that those very hardships were really the making of Man. To meet them successfully and so survive, he first became Man by rigorous natural selection of all those variations which added to the physical and mental capacities which now separate him from his nearer apelike relatives. Then, with those capacities, he aggressively and ingeniously made his predominant place in the world. It was perhaps always thus, and this last episode of hardships was but the final part of that longer harsh history of the physical world, which as it changed, brought both the hardships and the opportunities by which all Man's remoter ancestors evolved and climbed upward.

# CHAPTER 11

# LIFE ON THE PLANETS

WE know that life exists, and has long existed, here on Earth. But is there life on other planets? What are the conditions here on Earth which make life possible, and do such conditions exist on any other planet, or perhaps satellite, in our Solar System? And of course we inevitably ask those same questions about possible planets and their moons attending other stars in the Universe. Of them we can so far only speculate, for we have as yet no certain way of even knowing about them, the distances being too great for seeing such small and dim objects, lost in the overwhelming glare of their own suns. Yet we will do such speculating, perhaps all in vain. But first we will discuss the possibility of life under the conditions that we can and do find on the members of our own solar family. Of them we really do know much, though still not always enough to give fully final answers. Usually we can say "no" quite definitely, but on occasion it can be "maybe."

What are the conditions essential for the existence of life as we know it on a planet or satellite? We can sum them up in these few words: temperature, light, atmosphere, water, oxygen, carbon compounds, plenty of time, and the right past.

One thing we know about the stuff of life is that it is very complex and delicate. High temperatures break it down into simpler combinations of matter, always nonliving. Thus we can pasteurize milk by heating it for a time to a mere 150° F., thereby killing even the tough bacteria it contains, and we can readily sterilize water for safe drinking merely by boiling it. So where temperatures go over 150° F. (and certainly over 212° F., the boiling point of water), we need hardly bother to look for life to appear and persist.

On the other hand, low temperatures alone may not break up the stuff of life, but do halt its living activities, and if this continues, the life does end. For the processes of living depend on the use of energy, and here on Earth this is initially derived from the heat and light radiated by the Sun. So we must ask, for each member of our Solar System, whether it has a surface temperature between the freezing and boiling points of water. If not, forget it as a possible abode of life. For this reason our Sun itself is out, for its surface temperature is about 11,000° F., much too hot for the stability of most simple chemical compounds, to say nothing of the complex stuff of life.

### Solar Heating of Planets

But let us not then ignore the Sun; we still require it, off at a proper distance, for the needs of life. For from it the planets and their moons get virtually all their heat and light. In whatever manner they may have been born, they are all now well cooled down, at least at their surfaces where life must carry on. Radioactivity does supply some heat, but not nearly enough to balance loss into space once the heat reaches the surface. So the temperatures for life purposes depend on the heat and light now being received from the Sun, and the amounts of these depend primarily on distances from the Sun.

We have already learned (Chapter 6) that the farther a planet or moon is from the Sun, the less heat and light it receives, and the lower its surface temperature. And knowing the relative planet distances, we can readily figure the relative amounts of heat and light they receive, and thereby make good guesses at their probable surface temperatures. The results have already been summarized in Table A on Planet and Satellite Data. That table gives what we know of temperatures at the visible surfaces. However, for Venus and the giant planets Jupiter, Saturn, Uranus, and Neptune that means the outer surfaces of their cloudy atmospheres. On Mercury, Mars, and our own Moon (and perhaps the other planet satellites) we actually see the solid surfaces where life is most likely to occur.

Temperature conditions may, however, be modified by the rotation of a planet or satellite relative to the Sun. For example, Mercury, the planet nearest the Sun, rotates but once during each revolution, and so keeps the same side always facing the Sun, the other side being always in darkness. As a result, the eternally sunlit side never gets a chance to cool off, and the other side no chance to warm up. So the sunlit side is much hotter than the average we figure from relative distance alone, while the other side is much cooler. The sunlit side is well over 600° F., hot enough to melt lead, and certain to roast and char any living matter. Meanwhile the dark side is virtually as cold as space itself, several hundred degrees below zero.

In contrast, our Moon, though much like Mercury in some ways, does rotate once a month relative to the Sun, and its opposite sides have therefore opportunity to heat up and cool off in turn. The temperature differences are therefore not as extreme, though the slowness of the rotation does make the temperature changes very great indeed.

**The Planet Atmospheres**

Mercury illustrates another important factor in modifying surface temperatures, the presence or absence of an atmosphere. Mercury has no discernible atmosphere, being like our Moon in that respect. The reason, in both cases, is the smallness of the surface gravities, these in turn being due to the small masses. The surface gravity of Mercury is only 36 per cent that of the Earth, and that of the Moon only one-sixth, not enough in either case to retain an appreciable atmosphere.

If Mercury had an atmosphere, it would trap heat like the windows of a hothouse, letting in short-wave radiation from the Sun, but holding back the longer heat waves trying to get away, thereby raising the average temperature somewhat. On the other hand, circulation of an atmosphere would tend to equalize temperatures on the sunlit and dark sides, winds from the sunlit side carrying heat to the dark side, winds from the dark side carrying coolness to the sunlit side, thus tempering the extremes of both sides. On a nonrotating planet, however, those winds would be most violent because the temperature differences would remain extreme despite all the equalizing the winds could accomplish. On Mercury, nonrotating and lacking atmosphere, there is of course no tempering or equalizing of its extreme opposites of intense heat and severe cold.

In Chapter 6, we concluded that the computed surface gravities of the several planets and satellites should result in no atmosphere for our Moon, complete atmospheres for the Earth, Venus, Jupiter, Saturn, Uranus, and Neptune, and thin atmospheres for Mars and perhaps Pluto, the Jupiter satellites Io and Europa, and Saturn's big satellite Titan. All this is quite in accord with the facts as far as we can observe them.

Venus does have a considerable atmosphere, Mars a thin one, and all the giant planets apparently deep and dense atmospheres.

Those atmospheres of the giant planets lack our familiar oxygen, carbon dioxide, and water vapor, but do have nitrogen, the lighter gases hydrogen and helium, and a strong mixture of methane (the deadly marsh gas), making them all poisonous to living beings. Jupiter (Plate XXI) and Saturn show a lot of pungent ammonia gas, frozen out of the colder atmospheres of Uranus and Neptune. However, even a good atmosphere would not be enough for these distant planets, for their temperatures are too low for life to exist. Just as too high a temperature rules out Mercury as an abode of life, so excessive cold rules out all the planets and satellites beyond Mars. Also, because of their temperatures, the four giant planets have no water vapor in their atmospheres, it being frozen out into shells of ice thousands of miles surrounding their heavy planetary cores of rock and probably iron. Therefore, only the three planets Venus, Earth, and Mars could permit any form of life to exist. Earth we know about, so let us consider Venus and Mars more closely.

### Conditions on Venus

In many ways Venus is almost a twin sister of the Earth, only a little smaller in size, mass, surface gravity, and escape velocity of gases. Consequently, it retains a comparable amount of atmosphere, but because of its nearness to the Sun, receives nearly twice as much radiation, and is, therefore, much hotter, possibly even above the limit for the very toughest living things. It was long assumed that this intense heat is responsible for the heavy opaque clouds filling the atmosphere and always hiding the solid surface from our view. Yet both the atmosphere and the clouds are somehow strange, for studies with the spectroscope reveal practically no oxygen or water vapor, but much carbon dioxide.

It happens that carbon dioxide is a very effective heat trap, preventing loss of heat received from the Sun. This suggests that the actual temperature of Venus should be high, perhaps above 212° F., the boiling point of water. This has now been verified by Frank D. Drake of the new National Radio Astronomy Observatory in West Virginia, who announces successful radio penetration of the atmosphere of Venus over a three-year period, with indications of a surface temperature close to 585° F. From this we must conclude that Venus is quite arid, its ocean and other surface water completely evaporated. Under such heat and drouth, life just cannot exist, not even the lowliest vegetation. If there were vegetation present, it should have cleared the air of carbon dioxide and released into it oxygen as here on Earth. But under the existing conditions, any oxygen would be tied up chemically in the carbon dioxide on the one hand, and in the oxidizing of surface rocks on the other. This would also dispose of all the water supply, its oxygen getting thus tied up, its freed hydrogen probably escaping into space.

The heavy Venusian clouds can therefore not be water vapor, but rather dust. For at the high temperatures prevailing, great storms would always be going on, with winds of unheard violence sweeping over the desert surface, drawing the fine dry dust up into thick clouds swirling into the atmosphere for tens of miles upward, shutting off all view of the outside sky of Sun, planets, and stars. But there could of course be no eyes to miss these sights, for under the conditions we must infer on Venus, life cannot exist, not even plant life, and without plants, no animals either.

### Conditions on Mars

So now we are left with Mars as the only planet, aside from our own Earth, at all possible as the abode of life. (Plate XXII). But here our ears perk up, for we have all heard of Martians (even though fictional) and visible canals which might well be the works of intelligent beings. But however eager and expectant we may be, we must still examine the facts as we find them, and draw only such reasonable conclusions as those facts actually warrant.

Mars is a small world, roughly half the diameter of the Earth, about one-ninth its mass, with a surface gravity about 38 per cent and a gas escape velocity of about 45 per cent that of the Earth. This necessarily means a thin atmosphere extending up to perhaps fifty or sixty miles above the surface, but so rare it can weigh only a few per cent of our Earthly air. Because of greater distance, Mars receives only 43 per cent the intensity of solar radiation that we get, and so we must infer that its average surface temperature is much lower, say about $-40°$ F., but raised a bit by its scanty atmosphere serving as a heat trap, albeit a rather poor one. Our observations actually show noon temperatures up to $50°$ F. in the tropics, but falling off rapidly to $-130°$ at night.

Mars does have days and nights since it rotates once in 24.5 hours. Also it has seasons, for its axis of rotation is inclined to its orbit plane by 24 degrees, thus tilting its poles alternately toward and from the Sun in its year of 687 of our own days. Its general climate has been likened to a clear day on a high Earthly mountain, the temperature rising rapidly until noon as the Sun climbs higher in the sky, then falling off until sunset and through the night, the thin dry air having very little power to blanket and retain the surface heat.

Our attempts to determine the contents of the Martian atmosphere by spectroscopic observations have been quite thwarted by its extreme rarity, there being just not enough atmosphere to give us a trace of anything but perhaps a little water vapor. So if there is any oxygen, it is probably about a thousandth as abundant as in our own air. Carbon dioxide, we have reason to think, is more abundant.

However, the existence of such water vapor is well proven by the presence of polar snowcaps, very conspicuous even through a small telescope. These change with the seasons, appearing alternately during the northern and southern winters, melting away entirely during the summers. Judging by the small amount of heat received from the Sun and therefore available for melting away these polar caps, they are not very thick, perhaps only six feet at best, and down to mere inches at the margins.

It has been suggested that these white polar caps are not snow at all, but frozen carbon dioxide, popularly known as *dry ice*. But to stay frozen, dry ice requires a temperature of $-110°$ F., even at our higher atmospheric pressure, and still lower under the much smaller pressure on Mars. Our measured Martian temperatures are not nearly low enough for that. So the polar caps are undoubtedly snow, and that gives us another check on the temperatures which actually do prevail on Mars, averaging somewhere above $32°$ F., except in the winter polar regions.

Also in the Martian autumns we often see a haze of clouds over the edge of a polar cap, which then clears away, leaving the edge somewhat extended. What we have seen is, of course, the top of an autumn snowstorm. We also see clouds form elsewhere at all seasons of the year. These, however, are of two kinds, white and yellow. The white ones generally form soon after the Martian noon as the temperatures begin to drop, and, as the planet rotates, move to the sunset edge where they appear raised above the surface, up to an estimated twelve miles in the atmosphere. Here we are evidently watching the condensing of water vapor into clouds as the air begins to cool from its noonday high. By the next morning these clouds are generally gone.

The yellow clouds, on the other hand, linger on, sometimes for several days, are usually of wider extent, and occur at much lower levels in the atmosphere. They are probably dust storms stirred up by winds over the widely arid areas of the planet.

Even to the naked eye, the planet Mars is conspicuously red. From this, in fact, it derives its name, Mars being the bloody Roman god of war. The telescope shows that the greater portion of its surface consists of areas ranging from orange to dark red, probably deserts, which do not change with the seasons. Mars seems to have no real mountains, but the deserts may well be the higher and drier regions which surface and ground waters do not reach. Their reddish hue testifies rather eloquently to some oxygen in the atmosphere, but perhaps largely in the past, for that red is probably due to complete oxidizing of the rocks. In contrast, the rocky surface of our Moon is blue-gray, which means only partial oxidizing or none at all, there being no atmospheric oxygen available. On Mars it probably means that chemical combination has locked up most of the oxygen supply in the rocks, so that there is very little in the atmosphere itself.

The darker areas of Mars are greenish-gray, and do change with the seasons so as to suggest that they are covered with vegetation. Early observers thought these dark areas were seas, and named them so, but actually there are no open seas on

Mars. If there were, they would reveal themselves by mirroring shafts of sunlight to us when the seas were calm and the
angles of reflection right.

## Canals of Mars

In 1877, with Mars most favorably close to the Earth, the
Italian astronomer Giovanni Schiaparelli made a most startling discovery, the existence of a network of fine dark lines
over the so-called continental areas. Some were only a few
hundred miles long, but others extended for thousands of
miles. None were easy to see, while others were most elusive.
Their widths were estimated as ranging from a couple of hundred miles down to a mere twenty miles at the limit of
visibility. But most important, they seemed to be straight, and
they changed, often with the seasons.

Schiaparelli called them *canali*, which in Italian simply
means channels. But popularly, and even in the minds of
some astronomers, they were translated as *canals*. The
American astronomer Percival Lowell, for instance, took them
quite seriously and in 1894 built a fine observatory near Flagstaff, Arizona, largely to study Mars, and did some fine observational work. From 1906 on he thereupon published several
books to popularize his belief that the canals were actually
irrigation ditches drawing water from the melting snowcaps,
distributing it to raise crops to feed the population of intelligent beings who had presumably constructed these unnaturally
straight and therefore artificial engineering works for just this
purpose. As the waters flowed through them, Lowell contended, vegetation sprang up alongside them and so rendered
them seasonally visible.

Unfortunately for this exciting conclusion, many other

skilled observers, using even better telescopes, have been unable to see these so-called canals as straight lines, even broach-
ing the suspicion that the seeming straightness was a natural
optical illusion. In 1918 the Swedish chemist Svante Arrhenius
even questioned vegetation as the cause of the seasonal
changes, ascribing them instead to changes in color of certain
soils when water is added. But recent spectroscopic studies,
done independently by Kuiper and the Soviet astronomer
G. A. Tikhov, indicate the presence of lowly plant life similar
to the lichens of our colder Earthly zones. So the general
belief now prevails that the observed changes on Mars are
probably due to vegetation growing when watered by surface
flowage, or by rains brought by clouds, largely from the melting polar snowcaps. This, however, does not mean a general
acceptance of the canals as artificial channels dug by intelligent beings meeting the threat of general drouth by such a
planet-wide system of irrigation.

### Life on Mars

The Esthonian-born astronomer Ernst J. Öpik, now of the
Armagh Observatory in Northern Ireland, in 1956 advanced
perhaps the strongest reason for believing in Martian vegetation, namely the continued existence of the darker areas and
their seasonal changes. The argument runs as follows: The
redder areas are rather obviously deserts, from which the observed yellow dust storms must carry and drop a visible coating
of red-orange dust over the whole surface of the planet. This
would soon obliterate any dark area, unless a plant covering,
growing out afresh each year, could renew the areas of darker
green-gray which we see so distinctly. When, in addition, we

see the marked seasonal changes, with progressing renewal from the melting snowcap toward and beyond the equator, we apparently must assume that Mars has at least plant life responding seasonally to increasing warmth and moisture.

The existence of vegetation implies the presence of carbon dioxide, it being necessary for the processes of plant life and growth. Vegetation also implies some atomospheric oxygen, for it is regularly released by the plant life processes. But this does not necessarily mean that there is enough oxygen for the demands of animal life. For animal life, at least as we know it, uses up much energy, and in living Nature the synonym for energy is oxygen. Quite surely, the Martian supply of oxygen is extremely low, so low as to render animal life very unlikely. So until we have positive evidence of undoubted engineering works or intelligent beings, we must answer the question of animal life on Mars with a "No," but for plant life a likely "Yes."

When our space-travelers finally land on Mars, the plant life spread before them will undoubtedly seem most disappointing. Because of the harsh conditions, the plants will probably be only the most lowly and hardy, perhaps no more advanced than our lowest algae, lichens, and mosses in their adaptations to a tough environment. The oxygen supply will be most scanty, too thin even to permit lighting a fire. But the green plants can extract their own needed oxygen, and could doubtless adapt to hold it in storage for their own exclusive use. So too with the meager water supply, the plants could do what the cactus does, drawing by deep roots on the scanty ground water, and then storing it in swollen stems, thus perhaps invading the deserts with scattered growths. Also the extreme range of temperatures, estimated at about 180° F. from summer noons to winter nights, would severely limit plant growths and possible variations. Thus every advantage would have to be taken of the lesser sunlight. And the cold of winter (even of every night perhaps) would demand frequent passing into states of dormancy, with the life processes quite in abeyance, unless perchance the Martian plants can somehow store and use oxygen animalwise to maintain a sufficient internal temperature.

But as you must have already learned, it is often the way in science that just as we have arrived at a seemingly satisfactory conclusion, some newly discovered fact or novel theory comes along to upset everything or at least cast doubt. This has just happened to the idea of life of any kind on Mars. A trio of scientists of the National Geographic Society and the National Bureau of Standards, Doctors C. C. Kiess, C. H. Corliss, and Harriet K. Kiess, have just reported that many observed phenomena heretofore ascribed to life on Mars can be instead explained as due to chemical reactions and other effects of several oxides of nitrogen. Thus the reddish hue of the planet is explained by the absorption (and consequent non-reflection) of the green, blue, and violet components of sunlight by nitrogen peroxide. The polar caps are then chalky deposits of nitrogen tetroxide induced by cold, the dark borders about them being, not melting water, but liquid tetroxides and other nitrogen compounds. The oxides, frozen into tiny crystals, could account for the high white clouds, with the yellow clouds due to a higher concentration of nitrogen dioxide during a heat wave. If this explanation proves true, then life of any sort on Mars is quite impossible, since these nitrogen compounds are highly poisonous. But bear in mind that so far this new theory is still just a theory, and must be studied carefully in the light of all the known facts, before we can say with certainty whether there is or is not life on Mars.

### Observing the Planets

You may well wonder why we should know so little about the several planets, and why so much is rather uncertain. It is understandable enough that the planets Venus, Jupiter, Saturn, Uranus, and Neptune, with their thick and continuous cloud covers, should remain mysteries, since we cannot see through to their solid surfaces. And Mercury is small and far away, and being close to the Sun, hard to observe in the glare, showing barely enough surface features to disclose its slow rotation equal to its 88-day period of revolution about the Sun. Distance and smallness also keep us from seeing meaningful features on any of the satellites other than our own Moon. It we do see clearly, and photograph in such detail that the side we see is actually mapped more accurately than the surface of the Earth itself which we must step-by-step explore and laboriously measure. Yet even that detail of the Moon surface is not fine enough to disclose massive works of engineering, and certainly not the habitants who would have to construct such works.

So that leaves us only Mars with an observable planet surface. Again the great handicap is distance, Mars being some 34 million miles away even when nearest. This is roughly 140 times the average distance of the Moon. Its visibility, however, is much less than this would seem to indicate. Visibility varies inversely as the square of the distance, and must therefore be 1/20,000 that of the Moon. It is true that our giant telescopes can photograph much more distant and much dimmer objects such as faint stars and nebulae, but that is because these objects stand still for long exposures up to several hours. Mars, however, is rotating with an equatorial velocity of 550 miles per hour, and even an exposure of only a minute would mean a shift of over nine miles for some features on its surface. In addition, our own atmosphere is never still, and any object seen through it is never quite steady. Furthermore, magnifying the object to see more detail magnifies this unsteadiness. So we are limited strictly to much shorter photographic exposures, and in the end find that real detail is best disclosed by the sharp and trained eye at the telescope eyepiece, catching the rare instants of clearer seeing and steadiness.

### Earth Seen from Space

Yet it seems we should be able to see much more than we do, even on Mars. It is hard to realize how difficult the seeing really is, and we can perhaps get a better idea of the problem if we consider just what we could see of our own Earth from the very nearest of the other planets, Venus. The two planets pass in conjunction every 684 days and may come within 26 million miles of each other on occasion. This relative nearness should make our viewing about 1.7 times better than that of Mars. Also, looking at the Earth from an inner planet offers the advantage that we would see all the sunlit side of the Earth, rather than the mere crescent fraction that we see of Venus at its very brightest. In fact, our Earth seen from Venus should be six or seven times as bright as Venus ever appears to us.

We already know that it would be no use trying to observe from the surface of Venus because of its dense and continuous cloud cover. But the time should not be far off when one of our space rockets, approaching Venus and carrying a TV camera or a human observer, can permit a look back at the Earth. The naked eye will then see a bright sapphire-blue planet dominating the whole night sky, and close by, a much dimmer yellow satellite accompanying and circling about it.

A good telescope would easily show the Moon disc, but only as we see it through a pair of field glasses, and therefore not in very clear detail. But the views would include the "other side" of the Moon, which we now never see because it is always turned from us.

But just how much could we actually see and interpret on the face of the Earth itself? Surprisingly, perhaps, we would not see too well the outlines of the continents and oceans because of the atmospheric haze. We could draw fairly good maps of the fixed and gross features, but with uncertainties here and there. The ocean and other large water surfaces would appear as a deeper blue, and occasionally, when calm, and the angles were right, reveal themselves by brilliant flashes of sunlight. The conspicuous landmarks would readily disclose the rotation of the Earth and very precisely its twenty-four-hour period.

Very conspicuous would be the brilliantly white, but ever changing, cover of clouds. At times there would be wide expanses of continuous cover, hiding everything below, and materially increasing the brightness of the planet as a whole. More often there would be wide areas checkered with scattered white cloud flecks, revealing surface features momentarily between them. All clouds would be moving, and any continued observation would disclose predominant bands and directions of drift indicating belts of prevailing winds.

Close watching would also soon locate certain regions, such as the North Atlantic, where cloud masses seem to be born, and the knowing weatherman would infer that cold air masses there meet warm moisture-laden air to condense that moisture into clouds. Elsewhere our observer would see the clouds dissipate seemingly into thin air, perhaps evaporated by the

Sun's heat, or dispersed by the wind. Or he might guess that the cloud moisture had precipitated as rain, but he would be sure only when it fell as snow, leaving a white blanket, more or less permanent until it melted away. Very conspicuous would be the great snow- and icecaps about the poles, which would expand and retract at their margins with the seasons, alternating during the year between north and south.

Such alternate waxing and waning of the polar ice- and snowcaps imply an atmosphere for carrying the moisture back and forth. The clouds and their drifting give even more direct evidence of a shell of gas enveloping the planet, but its chemical composition could only be determined by careful spectroscopic studies. Positive proof of the atmosphere would be given when stars and Moon passed behind the Earth, for the transparent spherical shell would refract and displace the star images (prolonging visibility a bit) and distort the surface features of the Moon at the moments of disappearance and reappearance. Indeed, these refractive disturbances, carefully measured, would indicate both the depth and the density of the atmosphere. Furthermore, the refraction would result in a coppery-red ring of light about the planet as the Moon passed behind it, a prismatic effect familiar to us in red sunsets, and an orange Moon just rising above the horizon.

That reddening effect is due to the absence of the blue component of white sunlight scattered by the atmosphere. Here on Earth it gives us our daylight sky of scattered blue light. Viewed from afar, it would impart a blue tinge to everything upon the surface. The oceans would be a somewhat deeper blue. Areas of green vegetation would turn a bluer green. Misleadingly, bare brown earth would appear gray or very dark green, and the yellow of deserts a very light green. Even the white snow fields would be the pale blue that the knowing artist sees and paints into shadows on white snow.

The top surfaces of high clouds would be purest white, they having much less atmosphere above to tint them with the brush of blue.

### Indications of Life on Earth

From all these observations, our space-traveler, were he a stranger to the Earth, could rightly infer certain important conclusions. There is obviously a deep, dense atmosphere. The seasonal changes in the snowcaps would indicate a moderate temperature, low enough in winter for the freezing of water yet high enough in summer for its melting. There is an abundance of water, attested by the plentiful clouds, the snow-and icecaps, and the broad expanses of mirroring oceans. In short, the conditions would seem most favorable to the exist-ence of life.

Furthermore, he would find positive evidence for the pres-ence of life in the form of vegetation. Certain seasonal color changes (explained by the tilted axis of Earth rotation) would indicate such vegetation, by adding greens to the areas of growing crops and leafing forest with the coming of spring to North and South. And where there is vegetation, he would know that the atmosphere contained: first, carbon dioxide, needed by the plants; and second, some oxygen, given off by the plants.

All this would suggest the possibility of animal life as well, but of its actual presence the space-traveler would find no sign at that distance. None of Man's animal kindred would be large enough to be seen, nor would they produce animate effects at all visible. Even intelligent Man would show no sign. for even his greatest works would prove too small to be seen. His giant ships, his great engineering structures, his networks of highways, even his spreading cities and wide expanses of farmed fields, none would be recognizable at the vast distance and through the slight haze of atmosphere. Only if he were broadcasting the right radio signals, and the space-traveler could tune in on them, would there be any sign that Man existed upon this Earth.

However, if even plant life alone exists on Mars as well as the Earth, we must not overlook the importance of what it implies. It suggests that if anywhere the conditions for life do exist, such life is likely in due time to appear, presumably by quite natural processes.

### Other Stars with Planets

Encouraged perhaps by the present promising prospects of successful space travel in the near future, scientists have lately been speculating on the number of stars with planets, what portion of those planets could be habitable by plants and animals, and of course how many may be expected to have animals evolved to an intelligence comparable to our own. And lurking in everyone's mind is of course the question: Are those intelligent beings like ourselves in physique, behavior, and capacities?

Until recently, the hardheaded astronomers were very dubious about many stars with planets, largely because they thought that planetary systems were born only by collisions or near collisions between stars, which must have been very rare indeed because of the enormous distances separating the stars even in our crowded corner of the Universe. But lately all that has been changed by general acceptance of the von Weizsäcker-Kuiper theory of star formation by condensation from swirling nebular dust and gas clouds. Such an origin implies the normal formation of either a double (or multiple) star system without planets, or a single star with a family of planets. And as there are known to be millions of galaxies in the Universe, each with billions of stars, many of which are double or multiple, the guess now is that there are actually billions of planets too.

But we must ask what proportion of all those planets of outer space are likely to have the right conditions to make them habitable. A recent article by the Chinese physicist Su-Shu Huang, working in Washington in our National Aeronautics and Space Administration, attacks that problem. He points out it has probably taken life here on Earth some three billion years to evolve to the stage of human intelligence. For that to occur, our Sun must have been shining with quite constant intensity for at least that long. Furthermore, we now realize that unless a star falls in the Main Sequence of the H-R Diagram and has a mass not much greater than or less than that of our Sun, its planets would not have time to develop life thus far. Stars of greater mass would not last that long as they spend their energy reserves too fast, and those outside the Main Sequence are changing too rapidly to provide the constant conditions that life requires. As to the dim red-dwarf stars, he thinks that their light and heat are insufficient to maintain life on their planets. He therefore concludes that only planets of F, G, and K stars are likely to have well-developed life. But as those are the most numerous among the visible stars, there should be plenty of habitable planets available.

However, the actual seeing of such planets for close-up study is something else again. Not only will they be lost in the glares of their suns, but even to see a world the size of our Earth, at the distance of the very nearest star, would require, it has been estimated, a telescope a mile across and ten miles long, far beyond any present or early hopes for attainment. So we can still only speculate as to what proportion of all those planets of outer space have the right conditions of size, temperature, atmosphere, water supply, etc., to make them habitable. To be conservative, let us guess only 1 per cent. Even so, there must be tens of millions of habitable worlds.

### Life Through the Universe

This, of course, does not mean that those worlds are actually inhabited. For life to originate, according to current scientific opinion, it is not enough that conditions be right at the present moment, but also that the earlier planet conditions had to be right in rather different ways. In other words, the life of a planet depends upon a development of rather special conditions (largely as to atmospheric and ocean compositions) over long reaches of time. That naturally reduces the chances of life very considerably, though it still probably leaves us with millions of inhabited planets.

But what are the inhabitants like? Particularly, are they like ourselves—human in form and capacity? Or are those science-fiction authors nearer right who populate their planets of outer space with creatures utterly strange in shape, behavior, and mental attributes?

We have every reason to think that the inhabitants of other worlds are quite different from ourselves. For we find it most unlikely that the evolution of life forms elsewhere could duplicate in detail and results the story of life here on Earth. We know that actual story rather fully for the last half-billion years, and we are most certain that the shapes that we and our ancestors have passed through were the results, not of a planned progression to a predetermined form, but of merely a series of transitory adaptations to ever changing environmental circumstances, adaptations which were themselves genetic accidents. On any other world, the course of evolution would follow equally haphazard paths, giving rise to life forms which we would find wholly strange. Pursuing this thought in a lecture at the 1959 meeting of the American Association for the Advancement of Science, Herman J. Muller, the Nobelprize-winning geneticist, concludes that "to suppose human beings have evolved there is about as ridiculous as to imagine that they speak English."

Nevertheless, our space-traveler, landing on a distant world, might still find many familiar details of animal structure put together to make up strange inhabitants. The swifter creatures of the waters would probably be as streamlined as a fish. The flying creatures of the air, though not birds, or bats, or insects, would have wings, outwardly much the same, but differing probably in internal structure. There would be legs for walking on land, though whether two, or four, or six, or more, we cannot know until we see. Even eyes (the laws of optics being what they are) would probably follow the efficient basic camera plan which we ourselves share with such alien creatures as octopuses. Life elsewhere is therefore likely to consist of odd combinations of familiar bits.

When we come to consider the problem of the origin of life itself, regardless of its many forms, we will discover that among the apparently important requirements is lots of time. For as we review the history of our own Earth, it becomes evident that life was in fact a rather late-comer, and that for most of the long billions of years, the World was dead and barren, empty of even the lowliest life. And when, by happy combination of physicochemical circumstances, living matter finally emerged, it probably took something like a billion years before it became apparent in the geologic record, and even then took another half-billion years to evolve further to human intelligence which finally learns to understand its world and then reshapes it to its own uses. The time story as a whole, and the summary of life's earthly calendar, will be given in the next and final chapter.

# CHAPTER 12

## HOW LONG—PAST AND FUTURE?

In the year 1650, James Ussher, Protestant Archbishop of Armagh, Ireland, in a work entitled *Annales Veteris Testamenti*, announced a series of dates for Old Testament events, which dates, until our own time, have been printed in the margins of many of our Bibles. The chronology was based on Biblical references to elapsed periods and to ages of persons, which were then fitted and added together to fix the several dates. He placed the date of Creation in the year 4004 B.C.

Four years later, the learned Biblical scholar, Dr. John Lightfoot, Vice-Chancellor of Cambridge University, improved on this dating and wrote that "Heaven and earth, centre and circumference, were made in the same instance of time, and clouds full of water, and man was created by the Trinity on the 26th of October 4004 B.C. at 9 o'clock in the morning."

Unfortunately, later Biblical scholars of equal erudition and authority, using much the same methods, have variously placed this important date in the years 3760, 4710, 5411, 5503 and 5872 B.C., none however with such definiteness and finality as Dr. Lightfoot. Modern Bible historians now realize that the Mosaic account of Creation was borrowed from Babylonian and even older myths, was long transmitted largely by oral tradition, and cannot be relied upon for any such definite datings. In fact, our oldest written Mosaic account is from the ninth century B.C., and this was later combined with written versions even more recent, the whole taking its final form about 400 B.C. after many rewritings and known editings. As a result, modern religious scholars no longer rely on the Biblical account alone, but check its story and chronology at every point against other datings derived largely from archeological and historical studies of the entire Middle East area.

Furthermore, those archeological studies eventually established an antiquity for early mankind far greater than that indicated by the Biblical tradition. Meanwhile, research in geology and astronomy was bringing a realization that the World itself probably came into existence some millions of years ago rather than just a few thousands. This led the scientific-minded to seek new and effective methods for dating past geologic and related events.

### Age of the Oceans

The earliest of the scientific methods was suggested in 1715 by the English astronomer Edmund Halley, born in 1656, only two years after Dr. Lightfoot fixed the date of Creation so precisely. Halley is best known for accurately predicting the return of the comet which bears his name. But he was a versatile fellow who drew up the first tables of life expectancy, sailed the seas gathering magnetic and tidal data, and devised the method of estimating the age of the oceans, though he himself never tried to apply it.

Following an earlier explanation by Aristotle, Halley assumed that the ocean waters were originally fresh and had be-

come salty by the slow accumulation of salts washed down by
rivers flowing from the land into the sea. Rain water is fresh,
being evaporated by the Sun's heat from the surface waters of
the Earth, leaving behind any salts those waters may contain.
But as the rain falls over land areas and soaks through the soil,
it leaches away a small portion of the soil salts before it flows
away to join into rivers draining eventually to the seas. Because of this slight salt content, the waters of rivers and lakes
taste distinctly more palatable than the purer rain water. In
the end, of course, the salts accumulate in the oceans, and in
bodies such as the Dead Sea and Great Salt Lake, which lack
drainage outlets. The oceans and these landlocked basins lose
water only by evaporation, so their saltiness slowly increases,
up to a saturation limit of 36 per cent, when solid salt beds
form. The oceans, however, contain only about a tenth that
amount, of which roughly three-quarters is sodium chloride,
our common salt.

Halley suggested that the known amount of salts in the
oceans be divided by the amount brought in each year by the
rivers of the world, to give the number of years since the
oceans were first formed. But it is not at all easy to estimate
the average salt contents of the rivers and their total drainage
of water to the seas per year, so the resulting estimates for the
age of the oceans vary from ninety to six hundred million
years. And not only is the present rate of salt delivery hard to
determine, but we can be very sure it has not been constant
through the long geologic past. For we know that during
much of that past large areas of the continents were submerged under shallow seas, greatly reducing the land surfaces
being leached and drained by the rivers. This would of course
reduce the average yearly rate of salt transport and so increase
the presumed age of the oceans, up to perhaps some billions of

years. This, we will find, is quite consistent with results derived by more reliable methods.

While it is true that we know fairly well the amount of salt in the oceans of the world, it is not arrived at too easily. First of all it depends upon the volume of waters in the oceans, and measuring that took some centuries of exploring, mapping, and sounding of ocean depths, a task which is even now not fully completed. Also it is not enough to take a single random sampling of the percentage of salinity, for that varies from place to place. Thus the ocean waters near the outlets of great rivers are distinctly less salty, being diluted by the inflow of fresh river waters. Furthermore, near the equator and under the polar ice, the waters are saltier than the average. Near the equator this is due to the higher temperature and consequent faster evaporation which concentrates the local salt content. The freezing of salt water also leaves the salt behind and increases salinity. But water with more salt is heavier and therefore sinks, producing greater bottom salinity and giving rise to deep ocean currents. All these factors must therefore be considered to determine the present salt content of the oceans.

With such considerations kept in mind, the Halley method does seem legitimate enough, but scientific care also demands that one further source of doubt be at least pointed out. If the rivers have brought the salts to an originally fresh ocean, then the proportions of the ocean salts seem to be all wrong. In rivers, at present, 80 per cent of the salts are carbonates, 13 per cent are sulphates, and only 7 per cent are chlorides. In sea water, however, common salt and other chlorides make up nearly 90 per cent of all the salts. Some of this discrepancy can perhaps be explained by the extraction of the carbonates to form the shells of animals and lowly plants. Also it is possible that the ocean waters were never entirely fresh, which would quite upset any geologic ages arrived at by this method.

### The "Hourglass" Methods

Because of its apparent uncertainties, the ocean-salt method has been presented fully to show just how a seemingly clear and simple method may be fraught with upsetting factors. The same may be said of the whole general group of methods to which it is related, what we may call the "hourglass" methods. With the old-time hourglass our forefathers could measure the passing of an hour by first turning the glass upside down to bring its sand-filled bowl to the top, whereupon the sand would start flowing through a narrow opening and down to the bottom bowl, taking just one hour to do so. Meanwhile they could estimate elapsed fractions of the hour by the relative amounts of sand in the top and bottom bowls.

The geologists have long employed another such hourglass method based on the rates and amounts of land erosion on the one hand, and of deposition of sediments on the other. They of course have no convenient hourglass to turn over, but they can roughly estimate the rate at which the "sands" have flowed in the past, removed by streams from the land surfaces, to be then accumulated as sedimentary strata on the bottoms of the ancient seas. Theoretically, the amounts removed from the lands should equal those deposited in the seas. This should help somewhat in arriving at the amounts removed, it being obviously very difficult to estimate the amounts of land masses which are no longer there. On the other hand, amounts deposited are present to be measured, except that we often cannot tell what portions of such past deposits have themselves been eroded away. But scattered over the face of the Earth, we find deposits of the various geologic ages up to a total thickness of roughly one hundred miles. However, this may actually represent too little or too much. There are notable gaps in the geologic record, presumably periods of removal of previously deposited sediments, making our total too small. On the other hand, local deposits of great present thickness may be well above the average for their periods, thus exaggerating the total.

Estimating the proper rates of erosion and deposition is likewise most difficult and uncertain, partly because they are not even now uniform for different parts of the world. Thus, according to Arthur Holmes, geologist at the University of Edinburgh, the present rate of denudation for North America averages one foot in 8600 years, but for Great Britain one foot in 3000 years, a difference that greatly matters. We must also expect wide local variations in rates of deposition, such as rapid accumulations at the mouths of the Mississippi, the Nile, and other great rivers, far in excess of average shore deposits elsewhere. Furthermore, we may be quite sure that the sands of our geologic hourglass have not always run at a constant rate, for both erosion and deposition must have been much slower during past periods of continental submergence under shallow seas, when the land areas being eroded were much reduced in extent. Also the present rate of effective erosion is probably abnormally high because it is working with much loose surface materials ground up by the ice sheets of the recent Glacial Period.

From all this we would properly expect that estimates of the ages of the Earth and its rocks derived by this method would be much too low. And this is precisely what we find them to be. Up to the start of our present century, the ages of the oldest surface rocks were put at about 80 million years, though the Scotch geologist Sir Archibald Geikie in 1899 placed the minimum at 100 million and the possible maximum at 400 million, which maximum we now know from more modern methods to be much nearer the truth.

### Radioactivity Methods

Those modern methods, on which we now rely for fixing past dates, are mostly based on the rates of radioactive breakdown of certain unstable chemical elements. For the long-range estimates we largely use the heavy elements uranium and thorium, but there are also several other unstable elements, such as forms of potassium and rubidium, which are being increasingly utilized under special circumstances. For very recent datings we rely on carbon-14, a rare form of carbon. For intermediate datings, say between 50,000 and a million years, we have unfortunately had no suitable radioactive substances to work with until very recently.

The various radioactive elements have atomic structures which are for some reason unstable, and which therefore tend to change in one way or another. Such changes go on at average rates which we can determine experimentally in the laboratory, and can then use more or less confidently for dating purposes. For the over-all rates of change are apparently constant because unaffected by the ordinary conditions of temperature, pressure, and chemical change to which natural earthly deposits are subject.

Our general method of dating ordinarily consists in determining the ratio of the present to the original amount of the element, and from that and the known rate of radioactive breakdown, computing how long since it was originally deposited in its present matrix of rock material. However, the method varies somewhat in detail with the elements involved, and can be best illustrated by typical examples.

Thus the heavy elements uranium and thorium have atomic nuclei which break up spontaneously by throwing off, step by step, bits of matter and energy. Among the bits of matter are the nuclei of helium atoms, which then join with any available electrons to form normal helium atoms. Also, by the several steps of change in the original nuclei, a series of transitory elements are formed one after the other, until finally stable atoms of lead are produced, after which no further breakdown occurs. However, in a given mass of the element, only a few atoms are thus disintegrating simultaneously, but the proportion of those that do and their radioactive decay are such as to establish an over-all rate on which we can rely for our practical purposes of dating past ages.

Such a rate of decay for any given radioactive element is always described by the period of time in which a given amount of the element will be reduced to one-half. That period is then called its "half life." This means further that the remaining half will, in the second half-life period, be reduced to 1/2 of 1/2, or 1/4; in the third half-life period to 1/2 of 1/4, or 1/8; etc. For ordinary uranium, described by its atomic weight as U-238, the half life is about 4.5 billion years. For the rare uranium-235 used in our atomic bombs, the half life is only 0.7 billion years, while for thorium (Th-232) the half life is about 14 billion years.

The broken-down portion of the original radioactive element, as the result of its decay, becomes a related amount of each stable end-element, which has its own distinctive atomic weight. Thus the decayed portion of ordinary uranium becomes lead and helium, the lead having an atomic weight of 207 and from thorium the lead has an atomic weight of 208. In each case the helium had the atomic weight of 4.003.

In 1904, the English physicist Sir Ernest Rutherford suggested using the ratio of uranium and helium found together in ancient rocks to determine the ages of those rocks, on the theory that the older they were, the larger would be the ratio of the helium to the uranium. Computations based on the half life of uranium should then give fairly close figures for the true ages. Unfortunately, helium is a light gas very likely to escape from the rocks in which it is formed, thus giving uncertain ages which are normally too low.

So in 1905, the Yale physicist Bertram B. Boltwood instead took the ratio between the uranium and lead found together in the rocks of various geologic ages, and was soon able to announce that the ages thus figured were always consistent with the geologic order in which the several rock layers had been laid down, the rocks in lower geologic strata being always found older by the radioactivity method. Since then many workers in this field have applied the general method in a variety of ways, determining the half-life periods more precisely, separating the various end products more effectively, and using the several end ratios both apart and in revealing combinations, with ever more exact age determinations resulting. Up to the present, the results show that the very oldest rocks thus dated, which come from Manitoba, Canada, Western Australia, and Rhodesia in Africa, are from 2 to 3.5 billion years old.

Even these old rocks, however, do not indicate the full age of the Earth as a whole. First, they are only accessible surface rocks which we have so far found and tested for age. Undoubtedly there are others even older which we have not yet tested, or deeper and older rocks which we cannot even reach. Second, in both the uranium and thorium disintegration series, there is a radon stage. And since radon is a gas, which can escape from the rock, it may indicate too low an age. So getting at the total age of the Earth is both difficult and uncertain if we rely on this method alone.

But perhaps we can do better if we get at it indirectly. For example, astronomers assume that the meteorites which fall occasionally to the Earth's surface were formed at the same time as the Earth itself during the general formation of the Solar System. So they have tried to find the ages of the meteorites by testing their radioactivity ratios. The helium-uranium ratios indicate ages up to 4.8 to 10 billion years, but these are probably too high, for the abundant cosmic rays in space can produce extra helium, and may also increase the uranium decay rate, in either case exaggerating the meteorite age. The lead-uranium ratios, however, are probably more reliable and give ages of about 4.5 billion years. This is further confirmed by argon-potassium and strontium-rubidium ratios which give the same meteorite ages.

Comparable results are given by several other methods, some geological, others astronomical, which do not involve radioactivity. These methods are generally technical, depending much on the judgment of the trained scientist. Such, for example, are the degree of separation of the Earth's core from its mantle, the aging of globular and other star clusters and of our Galaxy as a whole, the tidal disturbance of double-star orbits, and the changes in stars as they use up their hydrogen supply and brighten, pulsate, or explode. All these, however, have led to the present consensus that the total age of the Solar System (and therefore of the Sun and Earth) is between 4.5 and 6.5 billion years, with an approximate doubling of that age before Sun and Earth fall victim to the disasters that stars and planets seem heir to.

### Carbon-14 Method

But before we get to those disasters we have two things to do: first, have a look at the carbon-14 method now so usefully employed for estimating short-range ages; and second, summarize the result of all our age determinations in the form of a geologic calendar for the Earth and its living inhabitants.

Carbon-14 is that rare form of carbon whose atom has a nucleus of atomic weight 14 instead of the normal 12. It is thought to be produced from normal nitrogen of atomic weight 14 by cosmic ray bombardment in the upper atmosphere. Such carbon-14 is radioactive, breaking down to ordinary carbon-12. Its half life, hitherto given as 5568 years, has just been revised by the United States National Bureau of Standards to 5760 years, with a plus or minus uncertainty of 200 years. The relation between its rate of production (presumed to be constant) and rate of decay is such as to leave a normal ratio of about one part of C-14 to a trillion of C-12 in our atmosphere, and therefore in the tissues of living things.

In 1946, Willard C. Libby of the University of California suggested that the C-14 to C-12 ratio could be used to determine the ages of articles composed of organic matter (all carbon-hydrogen compounds), which are preserved to us for a few thousand years. Originally, these two carbon forms would enter the living plant or animal in their ordinary ratio, but upon death, the proportion of C-14 would gradually lessen by radioactive breakdown. In the laboratory, by refined techniques, exacting skill, and delicate instrumentation, all the carbon is isolated, and the amount of carbon-14 still remain-

ing carefully measured by counting the radioactivity clicks by
means of a Geiger counter. That count, plus some mathematics, then tells the age of the given item.

Libby himself first tested the method by comparing its
results (here properly recalculated) with the known ages of a
series of ancient items. Thus a piece of wood from the funeral
boat of Pharaoh Sesostris III of Egypt, actual age 3750 years,
now gives a test age of 3746 (± 130) years. Pine-wood from
the Palace of Tayimat, Syria (age 2625 years), in a series of
three tests gives an average age of 2618 years. A Sequoia red-
wood, known by its growth rings to be 2905 years old, is
dated by three tests at an age of 3150 years. These and other
tests of the method are close enough to make it highly useful
for fixing many archeological and recent geologic dates. So a
number of carbon-14 laboratories have been set up and put to
work on a multitude of dating jobs. Here are some typical
results:

|  | Ages in Years |
|---|---|
| Hearth of Lascaux Cave, France (animal paintings) | 16,051 |
| Mud at end of glacier, Lake Knocknacran, Ireland | 12,193 |
| Peat, fossil man with elephant bones, Tepexpán, Mexico | 11,690 |
| End of glaciation, Irish glacial mud | 11,700 |
| End of glaciation, English mud | 11,225 |
| End of glaciation, German birch trees | 11,172 |
| Dung of Great Sloth, Gypsum Cave, Las Vegas, Nevada | 10,815 |
| Charred bison bones with arrowhead, Folsom, New Mexico | 10,224 |
| Man-made platform, lake shore, Starr Carr, England | 9815 |
| Fiber sandals, collapsed cave, Oregon | 9365 |
| Bones of sloth and horse, Strait of Magellan | 9310 |
| Land snail shells, ancient village, Jarmo, Iraq | 6938 |
| Wood of fish trap, Boylston Street, Boston, Massachusetts | 5172 |
| Wood from tomb of First Dynasty, Egypt | 5051 |
| Primitive corncobs, Bat Cave, Arizona | 2327 and 1812 |
| Linen wrapper of Dead Sea Scroll (Book of Isaiah) | 1983 |

From the above results, it should be noted that, because of its short half life, the datings by carbon-14 are practical only for comparatively short periods, though it is now hoped that by great refinement they may soon be extended to about 50,000 years. However, several other methods are now becoming usable, using effects connected with other elements. Thus fluorine has a visible effect on bones and permits sorting of bones deposited together, but gives only relative ages, not actual dates. Libby himself suggested use of tritium (triple-weight hydrogen), also produced by cosmic ray bombardment, but as its half life is only 12.5 years, its dating possibilities are very limited. Dating by silicon-32, with a half life of 121 years, is scarcely any better. But an entirely new method recently discovered by George C. Kennedy of the University of California, for determining the ages of rocks by their glow when heated, coupled with their radioactivity, now seems to hold considerable promise. And in the same institution, the team of Drs. Evernden, Curtis, and Kistler have been working with the potassium-argon method to determine dates of volcanic lavas within the last million years, thus hoping eventually to fill the dating gap. Unfortunately, being a gas, argon escapes easily from the rocks, so the few ages arrived at are minimum ones.

Yet so far, the radioactive dating gap still remains between some tens of thousands of years and a million or more. But in a practical sense, that does not much matter, for our present purposes at least. We have succeeded in the rough dating of the rocks that hold the evolutionary record of earthly life. What we have learned we now summarize to show dates, geologic periods, mountain-building revolutions, the important events in the evolution of life forms, etc., all so arranged as to bring out the several continuities, physical and living. The whole is then illustrated separately by dated charts giving

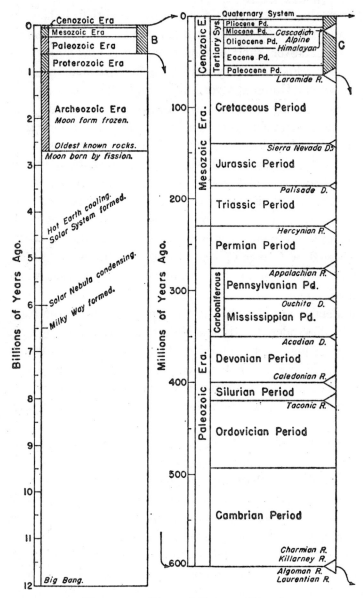

*Figure 20. Chart of Universe History*

A. Since Universe began. Recent portion magnified as Chart B.
B. Geologic History of the Earth. Recent portion magnified as Chart C of Figure 21.

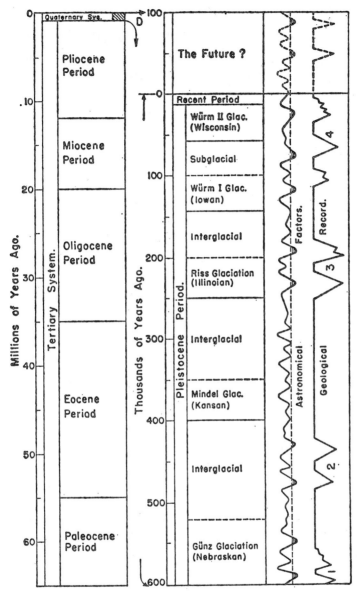

*Figure 21. Chart of Recent Earth History*

C. The Cenozoic (Recent Life) Era. Recent portion magnified as Chart D.

D. The Pleistocene and the Future.

a unified picture of all this past. In these charts, however, the earlier events are down at the bottom, just as we now find the earlier geologic strata at the bottom, all strata being normally in the order in which they were originally laid down. You must therefore read this chart from the bottom upward. In contrast, our story in words starts at the beginning.

### Calendar of the Past

The Big Bang occurred perhaps twelve billion years ago— unless Fred Hoyle is right, and the Universe is eternal and being continuously created in the form of hydrogen atoms. The date is mainly arrived at by dividing the estimated distances of the galaxies out in space by the speed per year at which they are receding from us. Our Milky Way is probably more than 6.5 billion years old, that being the age indicated for its globular clusters.

Then, sometime not later than 4.5 billion years ago, but more likely six billion, the Solar System was formed, with the Earth, its sister planets and their satellites, but perhaps not yet our Moon. The best dating seems to be by the radioactive ages of meteorites, with confirmations from other sources, astronomic and geologic.

Perhaps two or more billion years ago, our Moon may have been born by fission from the fast-rotating Earth, with subsequent slow recession to its present distance, and early freezing of its body into the slight egg-shape it has today.

Meanwhile on the earth, the *Archeozoic Era* begins. Its rocks, making up the Great Canadian Shield and other areas in Finland, Scandinavia, Africa, Australia, and northeast South America, were originally volcanic and sedimentary, but are now hard to decipher because greatly metamorphosed by heat, pressure, etc. The era ended with erosion so general as to indicate a long time gap (unconformity) before the record of the next era begins. The rocks, however, already show graphite deposits which suggest the beginnings of life.

By about one billion years ago the face of the Moon had already been battered into virtually its present pockmarked aspect, while on the Earth the *Proterozoic Era* began, with strata showing increasing aridity and wide areas of glaciation. During the next half-billion years there were several crustal uplifts marking Revolutions, named by the resulting ancient mountain ranges as Laurentian, Algoman, Killarney, and Charmian. Obviously much happened to the Earth-crust and surface, but life evolved slowly, our fossils showing only lowly forms of marine calcareous algae (limey seaweeds). Our best rock displays from this era are uncovered in the Grand Canyon.

### Era of Ancient Life

The *Paleozoic Era* began about 600 million years ago and lasted about 370 million years. Its name means *ancient life*, and its fossil record is so ample that we can divide it clearly into seven periods, each marked by its distinctive fossils. The first of these is:

The *Cambrian Period*, which lasted about 110 million years and was dominated by widespread continental submergence under shallow seas. Thus one great trough extended from Alaska to the Gulf of California, another from Newfoundland to the Gulf of Mexico. The Killarney and Charmian mountains, despite concurrent uplift, were eroded down about two miles to near sea level, while some forty thousand feet of sediments accumulated in the shallow seas, the bottoms of which were meanwhile sinking under the increasing weight. In these sediments we find the fossils of the oldest invertebrate animals, all marine forms, but we suspect that the first near-vertebrates were already evolving in the fresh-water streams, though their fossil remains are missing. Signs of glaciation appear late in the period.

The *Ordovician Period* began about 490 million years ago and lasted about seventy million years. In its shallow seas were laid down another forty thousand feet of sediments, but these were mixed with layers of volcanic ash. Life advanced in several elementary ways. Thus some simple forms took to living in colonies. Some invertebrates developed proper shells of lime, and small, rather harmless sea scorpions (eurypterids) appeared. We suspect that some plants took to shore life, the very first exodus from water to land. And above all, the first vertebrate (backboned) animals appeared, armored pre-fishes probably descended from some unidentified invertebrate group. This period ended with the Taconic Revolution, a great uplift of mountains from Newfoundland to New Jersey, during which the Ordovician strata were much folded and upended.

The *Silurian Period* began about 420 million years ago and lasted for about twenty million years, during the first half of which the Taconic Mountains were eroded down to their very roots. Again shallow seas were formed by continental submergence, with coral reefs indicating warm waters extending up to the Arctic Circle, though it should be remembered that there may have been considerable drifting of the continents since then to account for this. The sediments, to a total depth of fifteen thousand feet, were both shallow-sea and delta deposits. Some of the land areas were arid deserts. Among the invertebrates, more complex shells appeared, but more important, the eurypterids (sea scorpions) grew big, fast, and aggressive, becoming dangerous enemies of the primitive fishes. Some eurypterids took to the land as the first air-breathing animals, the land scorpions and millipedes. Among the vertebrates, lungfishes appeared, a promising step toward air-breathing. The period ended with the Caledonian Revolution, the uplift of the Scottish Highlands, with extensions to North Ireland, North Greenland, Spitsbergen, Norway, and other ranges across France, Germany, and Austria, in North Africa, and in Siberia.

The *Devonian Period* began about 400 million years ago, lasted about 50 million years and is again characterized by shallow seas, followed by mountain-building described as the Acadian Disturbance, too small to be dignified as a Revolution. The invertebrates multiplied in both numbers and kinds. The primitive fishes (ostracoderms) diversified, and ganoid (enameled) fishes developed towards the amphibia who climbed out of the water onto the shore as the first real land vertebrates. We find no actual amphibian fossils, but we do think we have one amphibian footprint left on a mud flat now become stone. The Devonian strata, up to twenty thousand feet in thickness, have been well studied, and consist of worn stones and sands, and mud shales laid down in quiet water, alternately submerged and exposed during wet and dry seasons, and when exposed, rusted to the red of the celebrated "Old Red Sandstone." Interlarded with these were certain green-gray strata never thus rusted by exposure above the water. Mid-Devonian climates were extreme, with lowland deserts of wind-blown sands, and annual drouths and floods producing lakes and ponds alternating with mud flats. This is the probable reason for some fishes becoming amphibians: having been caught in the shore pools which then dried out, they survived by somehow developing air-breathing lungs, makeshift to start with, but ultimately full-fledged and permitting continuous land life.

The *Mississippian or Lower Carboniferous Period* started about 350 million years ago, lasted about 40 million years, is characterized by deposits in shallow seas, bays, and deltas, and ended with the Ouachita Disturbance. The climate was semiarid as shown by the deserts, landlocked salt lakes, and dry-cracked mud flats left after short-lived floods. We find fossils of new forms of single-celled animals with hard shells, of echinoderms (relatives of the starfishes), of very primitive sharks, and most important, of fishes with fins converted to compact paddles with bony supports, muscles, and ball-and-socket joints for the figure-eight movements of proper walking. But of the four-footed amphibian walkers on the land, we have only their foot prints on the mud flats.

The *Pennsylvanian or Upper Carboniferous Period* began about 310 million years ago and lasted only 35 million years, during which the sea level (or rather the continents themselves) oscillated up and down, with a resulting alternation of sea, swamp, and land deposits, the period ending in vulcanism and a mountain-building uplift, the Appalachian Revolution. The fossils include many new marine mollusks, land snails, scorpions, spiders, cockroaches, and dragonflies (probably the very first fliers). The sharks developed somewhat, and we now find many amphibians, some up to 15 feet long with a 2 1/2-foot stride. The temperatures of Europe and North America were up about 20° F., with warm water corals growing up to Spitsbergen. Vegetation flourished (much of it in standing water), including giant horsetails, tree and seed ferns, and scale-trees four to six feet in diameter and up to a hundred feet tall. These, when they fell, were protected from decay by the swamp waters, and piled up to become in time the great coal beds of our present world.

May linger to renewal for
Part 9 the Genue to prepare
remarks about Mr. Wezel, the
will be in clue for that

Form No. 100

# CORRIDOR PASS

Date_ 10/30 _____ Time_ 2nd ___ over

Student_ Ginger _____

from_ his _____ to_ gym _____

Signed_ Mr Zur _____

Excused_____

Time returned_____ Signed_____

This pass must be returned to the teacher from whose room you were ex

School Service Co., Inc., 157 W. Ontario St., Chicago 10, Ill.

The *Permian Period* (last of the Paleozoic Era) began about 275 million years ago and lasted about 45 million years. An inland sea in the Great Plains region was followed by a salt dead-sea, then by red mud flats and chilly deserts and widespread glaciation, there being an average temperature drop of about 20° F., due perhaps to a general continental uplift, across eastern England, Germany, and northern France, with folding and mountain-building in the Urals and particularly the Appalachians. Perhaps the Permian record shows us the progress of at least the early stages of a mountain-building revolution, during which conditions become hard and trying for living things, wiping out old forms, and imposing severe selection resulting in forms more fit to survive. As a result, many invertebrate stocks disappeared, and our modern types of insects arose. The early amphibia also became extinct and the first reptiles appeared. Among the plants, horsetails and cycads predominated. The period (and the Paleozoic Era) ended with the Hercynian Revolution of mountain-building in Central Europe.

### The Middle Life Era

So drastic were the changes in life forms wrought by the hardships of the Permian Period that geologists describe the next era as the *Mesozoic* (meaning middle life). It began 230 million years ago and lasted 165 million years. It is divided by uplifts into three periods, Triassic, Jurassic, and Cretaceous, but as a whole is described popularly as the Age of Reptiles.

The *Triassic Period* lasted about 45 million years, recorded in a 25,000-foot depth of fresh-water and marine deposits, plus lava flows, among them those of the Palisades of the Hudson. On land were modern insects, in the waters modern corals and bony fishes. Everywhere the reptiles ruled, early dinosaurs on the land, streamlined ichthyosaurs in the sea, flying pterosaurs in the air. And potentially important, small reptile-like mammals lurked inconspicuously in the background.

The *Jurassic Period* began about 185 million years ago and lasted about 35 million years. The deposits were marine, plus wind-driven sand and dust. World-wide warm and humid climates produced lush vegetation, all evergreens, much alike over the whole world. The seas had giant mollusks, great sharks, and modern fishes. The reptiles expanded their domain, and gave rise to the first primitive birds. The period ended with the Sierra Nevada uplift and revolution.

The *Cretaceous Period* began about 140 million years ago, lasted 75 million years, and was marked by shallow seas in North America, Africa, and Asia. The plants were ferns, cycads, ginkgoes, and conifers, plus the new and rising flowering plants. The sea life of invertebrates and fishes became more modern. The dinosaurs diversified into new and strange forms, but on the whole were on the way out. The period (and the Mesozoic Era) ended with the great Cordilleran uplift and Laramie Revolution.

### The Recent Life Era

The last of the great geologic eras, merging into the present, is the *Cenozoic (or recent life) Era*. It began about 65 million years ago, and is divided into two Systems, the Tertiary and the Quaternary. The Tertiary System has five periods, and the Quaternary two. Their names (and the millions of years since each began) are:

*Tertiary System*
| | |
|---|---|
| Paleocene Period | 65 |
| Eocene Period | 55 |
| Oligocene Period | 35 |
| Miocene Period | 20 |
| Pliocene Period | 12 |
| *Quaternary System* | |
| Pleistocene Period | 0.6 |
| Recent Period (postglacial) | 0.011 |

The *Cenozoic* was an era of irregular continental uplift and mountain-building, in North America of the Rockies and coastal ranges, in South America of the Andes, in Europe of the Alps and Apennines, in Asia of the Himalayas, with climates generally warm. It opened with a "time of great dying" which is not really understood, during which many life forms disappeared, on both land and sea. Thus the dinosaurs were replaced by the early forms of mammals and birds, with only a few reptile groups surviving. Throughout the era, the mammals multiplied and diversified, becoming ever more modern. Among them were many odd forms, but for us the most important were the primitive insectivores, small and seemingly of little account, but destined to evolve to ambitious careers as monkeys, apes, and finally men. The Pleistocene of invading ice sheets and the severely selective hardships finished the job of man-making, picking and choosing those with the alertness, skills, and resourcefulness which we sum up in the word *brains*.

But the story of all that evolution, from life's very beginnings up to masterful man, is not the subject of this book. Here our story is of Physical Evolution only, from Universe beginnings down to our Sun and Earth, and how the Earth was rendered habitable by life, of first concern for our human selves. And we have brought that story right up to the present, and that would seem to be its End.

### The Foreseeable Future

But of course we realize that the Present is not really the End, and so our wide-awake imagination leads us to add another Period to our Geologic Time Table, namely the Future. And about that we have a deep curiosity which asks what that future will be like and how long it will all last.

We did some weather forecasting in Chapter 10 on Climates, and foresaw a future cycle of ice sheets invading our now temperate climes, but we were torn between two rival theories, one making it a few thousand years from now, the other some tens of thousands. And of other geologic events of the future we must be even more uncertain. Of only one thing geologic can we be quite certain, and that is repetition. We can be quite sure that continental lowlands will again sink below shallow seas (probably because of substratum melting by radioactive heating), those seas filling with sediments eroded and washed down from land elevations. Continents will probably shift and substratums freeze to solidify and thus uplift the continents so that strata are folded, mountains are built, and the shallow seas caused to retire from the lowlands. With rise and fall in elevations, and continents drifting from zone to zone, climates will change, and life forms will alter, but now (for a while at least) man will be taking part, and no doubt will modify events and effects in minor ways.

How long the Earth will remain fit for Man's survival is the greater question. It surely depends largely on long-term astronomic events which are probably far beyond his midget powers of control. It may of course be subject to unpredictable accident, such as collision of the Sun with another star (extremely unlikely), or the crashing fall of some great meteorite or asteroid upon the Earth (possible, but not too likely). But without accidents at all, there are certain astronomic trends which seem ultimately to so doom the Sun and Earth that Man must become extinct, if meanwhile he has not found himself another planetary home elsewhere in the Universe.

In Chapter 7 on the Career of the Moon we discussed such a long-term probability when the Moon, after some tens of billions of years, would approach the Earth so closely that the ocean tides, high and swift, would sweep from the Earth all vestiges of life. But it was also remarked that long before this could happen, the Sun would have so changed in its energy output that the Earth would be no longer habitable. So the story of the Sun itself therefore takes precedence in deciding how long our human future can possibly last.

That story is told us recently by Allan Sandage of Mount Wilson and Palomar Observatories, who bases it on our modern knowledge of the aging and life expectancies of the stars. Our own Sun is a star and derives the energy it pours out so profusely from the slow conversion of mass into energy as its supply of hydrogen transmutes into helium. As it thus ages, the percentage of hydrogen is reduced and that of helium increased, and that in due course will make a lot of difference. The rate of aging, as we learned in Chapter 4, depends on the original mass of the star, the larger ones using up their fuel supply at a faster rate, spending their substance in a shorter life. For a star the size of the Sun, the total life expectancy is about twelve billion years. As Sandage thinks the Sun began some six billion years ago, he concludes that it has another six billion years to go. We are rather lucky, he thinks, for if the Sun were only 10 per cent heavier, its total life expectancy would be only six billion years, and we would already be through.

But things will not stay uniformly the same during the six

billion years we have ahead. For the increase in the percentage of helium in a sun causes two basic things to happen in order to preserve internal stability. The Sun must both expand in size and increase in luminosity, which means that it will pour out more energy and that the Earth must become slowly warmer. By the end of the six billion years, this should raise the average Earth temperature by about 36° F. We will all probably have to move closer toward the cool poles, and perhaps by that time can ourselves evolve adaptively to live with comfort in the tropic heat.

But finally, at the showdown six billion years from now, what may we expect will happen? The answer is not reassuring. For the Sun's helium will have reached a critical amount, about 12 per cent of the solar mass. Then, within a half-billion years, the aging Sun will expand to thirty times its present diameter, fiercely burning its hydrogen fuel at an extravagant rate, with the Earth temperature rising by 900° F., evaporating the oceans and of course burning up all living things. At such temperatures it will also dissipate much of its substance into outer space. Only then, all the damage being done, will the spent Sun start cooling rapidly, until the oceans (if any water remains) again condense and freeze solid upon a lifeless world. In the end the Sun will settle down to one of those small and compactly massive White-Dwarf stars which seem to be the beginning of the end for normal stars, the ultimate end being progressive cooling to cold dark cinders. In this fashion, throughout the Universe of stars, the lights may be expected to go out one by one.

Yet there is another possible end to this story which at first seems a bit brighter. Yet it is not really brighter for us, as it does not alter the destinies of our individual Sun, our Earth, and ourselves. It may well be that as the old stars age and die, new ones will be born in the dust clouds of the galaxies. Or taking an even longer view, it may be that the Universe is being continually recreated in the form of hydrogen atoms, as Hoyle maintains, by some natural process which he cannot yet explain. Then, as the old lights go out, they will be replaced by fresh ones, with the starry sky thus ever renewed.

So for the present the grim outlook seems to be that we ourselves have only some six billion years ahead of us. But just as we settle down to a good worry about this, our selfsame Dr. Sandage announces new observations made on a dim star cluster, the age of whose stars appears to be already more than twenty billion years. And as if this were not enough, Dr. Fritz Zwicky, also of Mount Wilson and Palomar Observatories, has just reported that a study of the cores of the Milky Way and other galaxies indicates that not less than a million billion years was needed to form and age them. As this is merely the *least time* required, it suggests that sort of eternity called for by the Steady-State universe of Hoyle and his associates. To check on all this, the study of the Milky Way core is to be continued, using the very deep infrared rays which can penetrate through all the intervening dust clouds.

That million billion years represents a galactic life-span some 100,000 times that of the stars such as our Sun. With that we perk up and take heart, since galaxies, if not stars, can live so long. However, it also gives us a feeling of uncertainty in our reliance on these scientific speculations and forecasts. But to that we must become reconciled, for such is ever the way of our growing science, it never pretends to know what it does not surely know, and its conclusions are never final and infallible. Yet it does always progress toward ever increasing truth, step by step, tentatively, exploringly.

So too it must of course be with this up-dated scientific story of creation; it will certainly be revised further as we seek and learn more. Yet we can today feel fairly assured that we are at least approaching the truth, that the main outlines of the story are probably right as now told, and that its future revisions will be largely in details.


### Facing the Future

As it now stands, that story of the Creation of the Heavens and the Earth does imply some clear conclusions and pose some fundamental problems which Mankind sooner or later must face. Time is long and in our vast Universe our Earth is very small indeed. Certainly time past has been very long, and probably so will be its future. And the Earth is really smaller even than it seems, for only a mere fraction of its surface is habitable and several of its important natural resources are both limited and irreplaceable except by substitution.

As cosmic and geologic time goes, Man is just a newcomer on this Earth, but already he has heedlessly wasted vital resources and by unchecked prolific breeding threatens to crowd himself into a state of worldwide impoverishment. Only now at last in this clearer day of scientific understanding is he beginning to concern himself with the long tomorrows ahead and to plan intelligent steps for preserving and replacing the World's resources and potentials.

Most urgent of all is his need to learn tolerance and calm in meeting the international problems in his crowded World, lest he go on from cold wars to hot, and by impulse or accident exterminate all human kind by A-bomb or H-bomb, radioactive fallout and bacterial warfare. But once he can safely pass this present perilous moment, he can undoubtedly go on by worldwide collaboration to make the most of all the great potentialities of both his World and himself.

Then the remoter disasters of natural origin which the future seems to threaten can be faced with equanimity. There may again come ice sheets creeping inexorably down upon Man's habitations and proud works, but he will have good time to retreat equatorward and so survive. And long in the future, he may find the solid crust beneath his feet again sinking and in large part submerging under shallow encroaching seas, but there will still be higher ground on which to climb for the long precarious period of difficult survival before the continents once more emerge and new mountains uplift to restore the solidity on which to stand and build firmly. That Man will still be here seems assured, but it will depend upon his preserving that high resourcefulness which above all first made him Man. Perhaps his capacities will even be equal to the final problem of human escape to some New World elsewhere in the Universe before the Sun begins to swell and grow so hot as to burn our good Earth into a lifeless cinder. But should Man nevertheless fail to escape this final disaster, let us bear in mind that this will be still some six billion years from now, and that meanwhile there will be a myriad generations, each generation counted in billions, of those who will sample that opportunity we call life. The concern of our own and future generations had better be, not with worries over remote and problematical disasters, but with finding those practical ways for filling the lives that are to be with the maximum of satisfactions.

# INDEX